Ncb   80 + 81

P,   1, 3, 4, 7, 8, 10

3/840

01
61
61
65
50

09976

29712

61163

MATHEMATICS

in

AGRICULTURE

PRENTICE-HALL MATHEMATICS SERIES

Dr. Albert A. Bennett, Editor

MATHEMATICS
in
AGRICULTURE

R. V. McGee

Department of Mathematics
The Agricultural and Mechanical College of Texas

SECOND EDITION

PRENTICE-HALL, INC.

Englewood Cliffs, N. J.

Current printing (last digit):

16   15   14   13   12   11   10   9   8   7

L. C. Cat. Card No.: 54-5788

Printed in the United States of America
5 6 2 5 2-C

PREFACE TO THE SECOND EDITION

In recent years there has been an increasing demand for a practical book on mathematics designed especially for persons interested in agriculture. This book is the result of an earnest effort to meet that demand. In order to provide problems with appropriate and realistic settings, much reliable material pertaining to various phases of agriculture has been included. Also, a store of useful agricultural data is contained in the tables at the end of the book.

Improvements undertaken in the revision include the following: increased emphasis on problems arising from the use of machine power and electricity on the farm; modification of problem data in the light of current prices and practices; expansion of the treatment of algebra; and the screening of problems on the basis of their significance in agriculture.

The author wishes to express his sincere appreciation for the many helpful suggestions and criticisms received from members of the staff of the Agricultural and Mechanical College of Texas regarding the preparation of this book.

R. V. McGee

CONTENTS

x   CONTENTS

CHAPTER 1

MATHEMATICAL OPERATIONS

In its simplest form the word *mathematics* applies to man's *number work*. From its very beginning and throughout most of its development mathematics has been closely associated with man's everyday living. And as the student of today stands amazed at the extensiveness of the scope of mathematics and perhaps confused by the complexities of its processes, he may find satisfaction in realizing that mathematics is man's own invention. Indeed, mathematics may rightly be acclaimed as man's most valiant effort to deal mentally with his environment.

Fundamental Operations

While *counting* is undoubtedly the *original* operation of mathematics, it is common practice to label as fundamental the four derived operations of *addition, subtraction, multiplication*, and *division*.

A result obtained by addition of numbers is called a *sum*; a result of subtraction is called a *difference*; a result of multiplication is called a *product*; and a result of division is called a *quotient*. Thus, the sum of the two numbers 10 and 2 is 12; their difference is 8; their product is 20; and, if 10 is divided by 2, the quotient is 5; while, if 2 is divided by 10, the quotient is $\frac{2}{10}$, or $\frac{1}{5}$.

Practically all steps taken in solving problems included in this book involve the above operations and no others. Expressions like "canceling numbers," "dropping numbers," and "transposing numbers" do not identify mathematical operations, and the student will do well to avoid using such phrases.

In performing operations with numbers we show the same regard for kinds of units involved as we do in dealing with quantities expressed in terms of physical units. In combining the lengths of three boards whose separate lengths are 5 ft, 2 ft 9 in., and 20 in., we may either add like units and express the result in feet and inches, or express all

1

lengths in terms of a common unit and give the result in feet or in inches. These procedures are shown in the following.

	5 ft		5 ft	= 5	ft	5 ft	=	60 in.
	2 ft	9 in.	2 ft	9 in. = 2	3/4 ft	2 ft	9 in. =	33 in.
		20 in.		20 in. = 1	2/3 ft		20 in. =	20 in.
	7 ft	29 in.		8 17/12 ft				113 in.
or	9 ft	5 in.	or	9 5/12 ft				

Similarly, in combining whole numbers we combine separately the *counts* of *ones*, *tens*, *hundreds*, etc. Thus we may interpret the addition of 83, 574, 6, and 20 as follows.

$$83 = \qquad\qquad 8\ tens\ +\quad 3\ ones$$
$$574 = 5\ hundreds\ +\quad 7\ tens\ +\quad 4\ ones$$
$$6 = \qquad\qquad\qquad\qquad\qquad 6\ ones$$
$$20 = \qquad\qquad\quad 2\ tens$$

Adding, we get

$$5\ hundreds\ +\ 17\ tens\ +\ 13\ ones$$

which may be rewritten as

$$6\ hundreds\ +\quad 8\ tens\ +\quad 3\ ones$$

or as

$$683.$$

It must be admitted that manipulative skill developed through practice makes it unnecessary for most students to give such close attention to this matter of units in dealing with whole numbers. However, the author feels justified in presenting the above illustration because it points the way toward a proper consideration of units in operations involving fractions (common and decimal), mixed numbers, and the various number representations of algebra.

Abstract and Concrete Numbers

All numbers are abstract, in the sense that they have none of the properties of physical objects. However, a number expression that represents a quantity of some kind, as 5 lb or 3 in., is usually referred to as a concrete number. A so-called concrete number may be thought of as consisting of an abstract number times some specific unit of measure. In the expression *5 lb*, 5 is abstract and indicates the number of times the unit, *pound*, is taken in measuring the weight of some object or the magnitude of some force.

Strictly speaking, arithmetical operations are performed with abstract numbers only. For instance, to find the total weight of two objects, one of which weighs 5 lb and the other 3 lb, we add 5 and 3 and get as a result the abstract number 8, and then conclude that the weight of the two objects together is 8 lb. However, in practice concrete numbers themselves are frequently connected by signs of addition, subtraction, and so on, as if the operations were to be performed with certain quantities instead of with the abstract numbers which are the measures of the quantities. Thus, one may write 5 lb + 3 lb = 8 lb.

Numbers, as originally devised by man, represent mental concepts of *quantity*. They are expressions of *size* or *magnitude* arising from a *count* or *measure* of some kind.

Whole Numbers, Fractions, and Mixed Numbers

Numbers used in counting like 6, 29, 17, 354, and so on, are called *whole numbers* or *integers*.

A fraction is an indicated division of one number by another. Thus $\frac{5}{8}$ is a fraction in which it is indicated that 5 (called the *numerator*) is divided by 8 (called the *denominator*). Also, since $\frac{5}{8}$ is equivalent to 5 times $\frac{1}{8}$, we may consider the denominator 8 as *naming* or indicating the unit, $\frac{1}{8}$, being used, and the numerator 5 as being the *counter* of such units. It may be well here to remind the student of this fundamental principle of fractions: *The value of a fraction is not changed if its numerator and denominator are both multiplied by the same number or divided by the same number.* That number of course cannot be zero, since division by zero is impossible. Almost all work done with fractions is based upon this principle.

A number composed of an integer and a fraction taken together is called a *mixed number*. A mixed number is actually an indicated sum. Thus $16\frac{2}{3}$ is a short way of writing the sum $16 + \frac{2}{3}$.

Decimal Numbers

The word *decem* is a Latin word meaning "ten." Our system of arithmetical numbers is called the decimal system because 10 is the basic number of the system. For instance, the number 356 means $300 + 50 + 6$, or $3(100) + 5(10) + 6(1)$. If the student recalls the meaning of a positive integral exponent, and of zero as an exponent, he will see that this number may also be written as $3(10^2) + 5(10^1) + 6(10^0)$. Thus each digit of a number is a multiplier of a certain power of 10, the particular power depending upon the place that the digit occupies in the number. This decimal representation of numbers is extended further in the writing of mixed numbers and fractions by placing a period to the right of the 10^0 digit and considering the digits to the right of this period (or decimal point) as multiplying 10^{-1}, 10^{-2}, 10^{-3}, and so forth. It is well for the student to recall here the meaning given to a negative exponent. For example,

$$10^{-1} = \frac{1}{10}, \; 10^{-2} = \frac{1}{10^2} = \frac{1}{100}, \; 10^{-3} = \frac{1}{10^3} = \frac{1}{1000}, \text{ and so forth.}$$

The number 7356.482 may now be considered a short way to write the sum

$$7(10^3) + 3(10^2) + 5(10^1) + 6(10^0) + 4(10^{-1}) + 8(10^{-2}) + 2(10^{-3}),$$

or

$$7000 + 300 + 50 + 6 + \tfrac{4}{10} + \tfrac{8}{100} + \tfrac{2}{1000}.$$

The names of the places most frequently used in writing decimal numbers are given in the following scheme:

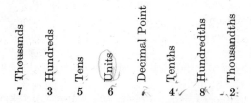

Thousands	Hundreds	Tens	Units	Decimal Point	Tenths	Hundredths	Thousandths
7	3	5	6	.	4	8	2

This number may be read, "Seven thousand, three hundred fifty-six, and four hundred eighty-two thousandths." In practice, it would usually be read, "Seven three five six, point, four eight two."

The following rules should be observed in performing operations with decimal numbers:

1. In addition or subtraction, write the numbers in a vertical column

with the decimal points aligned and add or subtract as with whole numbers.

2. In multiplication, multiply as if the numbers were whole numbers; then, beginning at the right, point off as many decimal places in the product as there are decimal places in all of the factors together.

3. In division, multiply both the divisor and the dividend by that power of 10 which will make the divisor an integer; divide as with whole numbers; and point off as many places in the quotient as there are in the dividend.

4. A common fraction may be changed to decimal form by dividing the numerator by the denominator, first placing a decimal point after the numerator and annexing as many zeros as desired. Common fractions (in lowest terms) whose denominators contain factors other than 2 and 5 cannot be expressed exactly as terminating decimals. Such fractions can be expressed decimally to any desired number of places.

The student will find the short methods of multiplication and division indicated below well worth learning.

1. To multiply a number by 10, 100, or 1000, move the decimal point to the right one, two, or three places, respectively, annexing zeros if necessary.

2. To multiply by 25, multiply by 100 and divide by 4.

3. To multiply by 50, multiply by 100 and divide by 2.

4. To multiply by 125, multiply by 1000 and divide by 8.

5. To multiply by 9, multiply by 10 and subtract the multiplicand.

6. To multiply by 11, multiply by 10 and add the multiplicand.

7. To divide by 10, 100, or 1000, move the decimal point to the left one, two, or three places, respectively, prefixing zeros if necessary.

8. To divide by 25, multiply by 4 and divide by 100.

9. To divide by 50, multiply by 2 and divide by 100.

10. To divide by 125, multiply by 8 and divide by 1000.

The student should see to it that he knows how to add, subtract, multiply, and divide with whole numbers, common fractions, mixed numbers, and decimal numbers, and should strive to develop accuracy and speed in performing these operations. In this connection, it is suggested that the student verify by actual computation the results obtained in the illustrative problems appearing in table form on pages 6 and 7. He may also practice on the group of preliminary exercises that follow. Such practice should refresh the student's memory of these important processes, and may provide for him a kind of self-examination of his readiness to proceed with the course.

Kind of Numbers	Addition	Subtraction	Multiplication	Division
Whole Numbers	$87 + 356 + 9 = ?$ $$\begin{array}{r}87\\356\\9\\\hline 452\end{array}$$	$3805 - 1847 = ?$ $$\begin{array}{r}3805\\1847\\\hline 1958\end{array}$$	$537 \times 48 = ?$ $$\begin{array}{r}537\\48\\\hline 4296\\2148\\\hline 25776\end{array}$$	$932 \div 37 = ?$ $$25\tfrac{7}{37}$$ $$37\overline{)932}$$ $$\begin{array}{r}74\\\hline 192\\185\\\hline 7\end{array}$$
Common Fractions	$\dfrac{4}{9} + \dfrac{5}{6} = ?$ $\dfrac{4}{9} = \dfrac{8}{18}$ $\dfrac{5}{6} = \dfrac{15}{18}$ $\dfrac{23}{18} = 1\tfrac{5}{18}$	$\dfrac{7}{9} - \dfrac{5}{12} = ?$ $\dfrac{7}{9} = \dfrac{28}{36}$ $\dfrac{5}{12} = \dfrac{15}{36}$ $\dfrac{13}{36}$	$\dfrac{5}{12} \times \dfrac{3}{4} = ?$ $\dfrac{5}{12} \times \dfrac{3}{4} = \dfrac{5}{16}$	$\dfrac{5}{6} \div \dfrac{3}{8} = ?$ $\dfrac{5}{6} \div \dfrac{3}{8}$ $= \dfrac{5}{6} \times \dfrac{8}{3}$ $= \dfrac{20}{9} = 2\tfrac{2}{9}$
	(a) $8\tfrac{2}{3} + 17 = ?$ $\begin{array}{r}8\tfrac{2}{3}\\17\\\hline 25\tfrac{2}{3}\end{array}$	(a) $43 - 19\tfrac{5}{8} = ?$ $43 = 42\tfrac{8}{8}$ $19\tfrac{5}{8} = 19\tfrac{5}{8}$ $23\tfrac{3}{8}$	(a) $12 \times 18\tfrac{3}{4} = ?$ $12 \times 18\tfrac{3}{4}$ $= 216 + 9 = 225$	(a) $6\tfrac{2}{5} \div 8 = ?$ $6\tfrac{2}{5} \div 8$ $= \dfrac{32}{5} \times \dfrac{1}{8} = \dfrac{4}{5}$

6

Mixed Numbers	(b) $8\frac{1}{6} + \frac{5}{8} = ?$ $8\frac{1}{6} = 8\frac{4}{24}$ $\frac{5}{8} = \frac{15}{24}$ $\underline{8 = \frac{24}{24}}$ $8\frac{19}{24}$ (c) $37\frac{3}{4} + 65\frac{5}{6} = ?$ $37\frac{3}{4} = 37\frac{9}{12}$ $65\frac{5}{6} = \underline{65\frac{10}{12}}$ $102\frac{19}{12}$ $= 103\frac{7}{12}$ $38.7 + 7.625 + .09 + 15 = ?$ 38.7 7.625 $.09$ $\underline{15.}$ 61.415	(b) $23\frac{5}{6} - 9\frac{3}{4} = ?$ $23\frac{5}{6} = 23\frac{10}{12}$ $9\frac{3}{4} = \underline{9\frac{9}{12}}$ $14\frac{1}{12}$ (c) $73\frac{4}{9} - 26\frac{7}{12} = ?$ $73\frac{4}{9} = 73\frac{16}{36} = 72\frac{52}{36}$ $26\frac{7}{12} = 26\frac{21}{36} = \underline{26\frac{21}{36}}$ $46\frac{31}{36}$ $73.5 - 26.72 = ?$ 73.50 $\underline{26.72}$ 46.78	(b) $12\frac{1}{2} \times \frac{3}{5} = ?$ $12\frac{1}{2} \times \frac{3}{5}$ $= \frac{\overset{5}{\cancel{25}}}{2} \times \frac{3}{\cancel{5}}$ $= \frac{15}{2} = 7\frac{1}{2}$ (c) $6\frac{2}{5} \times 3\frac{1}{3} = ?$ $6\frac{2}{5} \times 3\frac{1}{3}$ $= \frac{32}{\cancel{5}} \times \frac{\overset{2}{\cancel{10}}}{3}$ $= \frac{64}{3} = 21\frac{1}{3}$ $18.36 \times 4.7 = ?$ 18.36 $\underline{\times 4.7}$ 12852 $\underline{7344}$ 86.292	(b) $7\frac{1}{2} \div \frac{3}{4} = ?$ $7\frac{1}{2} \div \frac{3}{4}$ $= \frac{\overset{5}{\cancel{15}}}{\cancel{2}} \times \frac{\overset{2}{\cancel{4}}}{3}$ $= \frac{10}{1} = 10$ (c) $8\frac{3}{4} \div 6\frac{2}{3} = ?$ $8\frac{3}{4} \div 6\frac{2}{3}$ $= \frac{35}{4} \div \frac{20}{3}$ $= \frac{\overset{7}{\cancel{35}}}{4} \times \frac{3}{\cancel{20}}$ $= \frac{21}{16} = 1\frac{5}{16}$ $20.992 \div 6.4 = ?$ 3.28 $6.4\overline{)20.992}$ $19\,2$ $1\,79$ $1\,28$ 512 512
Decimal Numbers			

7

Preliminary Exercises

Perform operations indicated.

1. (a) $\frac{5}{12} + \frac{7}{18}$ (c) $\frac{8}{15} \times \frac{5}{12}$

     (b) $\frac{17}{20} - \frac{5}{8}$ (d) $\frac{4}{5} \div \frac{2}{3}$

2. (a) $16\frac{2}{3} + \frac{5}{6}$ (c) $15 \times 12\frac{2}{3}$

     (b) $42 - 7\frac{3}{8}$ (d) $18\frac{3}{4} \div 15$

3. (a) $27\frac{4}{7} + 13\frac{5}{6}$ (c) $5\frac{1}{2} \times 4\frac{2}{5}$

     (b) $31\frac{1}{8} - 6\frac{5}{12}$ (d) $72 \div 3\frac{3}{7}$

4. (a) $35.7 + 9.08$ (c) 6.25×2.8

     (b) $95.8 - 27.85$ (d) $106.5 \div 2.84$

5. (a) $47.85 + 32\frac{4}{5}$ (Suggestion: express $32\frac{4}{5}$ decimally.)

     (b) $63.5 - 17\frac{2}{3}$ (Suggestion: express 63.5 as $63\frac{1}{2}$.)

     (c) $8\frac{3}{4} \times 5.09$

     (d) $10\frac{5}{12} \div 1.25$

Use the short methods given on page 5 in obtaining the results of the following:

6. (a) 10×42.75 (d) 25×32

     (b) 1000×13.5 (e) 482×50

     (c) 100×250 (f) 125×0.72

7. (a) $3.5 \div 100$ (d) $780.5 \div 25$

     (b) $64 \div 10$ (e) $342.75 \div 50$

     (c) $83.7 \div 1000$ (f) $7500 \div 125$

8. (a) $\frac{3}{4}$ of $36 = ?$ ("$\frac{3}{4}$ of 36" is interpreted as meaning "$\frac{3}{4}$ times 36".)

     (b) $\frac{5}{8}$ of $18\frac{3}{4} = ?$ (d) 0.9 of $\frac{5}{18} = ?$

     (c) 0.042 of $500 = ?$ (e) $\frac{1}{2}$ of $\frac{3}{8} = ?$

9. (a) 8 is $\frac{2}{3}$ of what number? (The required number is $8 \div \frac{2}{3}$, which is 12.)

     (b) $16\frac{1}{4}$ is $\frac{5}{8}$ of what number?

     (c) 0.08 of what number equals 26?

     (d) What number times $2\frac{1}{2}$ equals 40?

     (e) 202.5 is $\frac{5}{8}$ of what number?

10. (a) 12 is what part of 15?   (*Ans.* 12 is $\frac{12}{15}$ or $\frac{4}{5}$ of 15.)

     (b) $7\frac{1}{2}$ is what part of 30?

     (c) $\frac{12}{35}$ is what part of $\frac{4}{5}$?

     (d) What part of 30 is 2.4?

     (e) What part of 65.7 is 19.71?

Problems*

1. Express the sum of 12 gal, 10 qt, and 13 pt in gallons; in quarts; in pints.

---

* Refer to the tables at the end of the book for information needed in solving problems.

2. Express the following sum (a) in pounds and ounces; (b) in ounces only; (c) in pounds only: 4 lb 12 oz + 3 lb + 9 lb 15 oz + 13 oz.

3. Add: $13.45, $0.80, $76, $9.75, 63¢.

4. $\frac{7}{8} + \frac{3}{4} - \frac{5}{6} = ?$

5. $65\frac{4}{9} - 37\frac{7}{12} = ?$

6. 480 ft 2 in. − 197 ft 10 in. = ?

7. Multiply $20\frac{3}{4}$ bu by 9.

8. 1 in. is what part of a foot? 7 in. is what part of a foot? 7 lb is what part of 12 lb?

9. 35 bu is what part of 210 bu?

10. $3\frac{1}{2}$ lb is what part of $24\frac{1}{2}$ lb?

11. 156 acres is what part of 390 acres?

12. A field containing $186\frac{3}{4}$ acres is divided into 9 equal plots. How many acres are there in each plot?

13. How many $2\frac{1}{2}$-bu baskets of corn are there in a crib containing 30 bu?

14. What is the weight of the water in a cistern that contains 464 cu ft?

15. How many bushels of wheat can be put in a bin that contains 900 cu ft?

16. How many gallons of water will it take to fill an aquarium containing $1\frac{1}{2}$ cu ft?

17. If a horse is 15 hands high, what is his height in inches?

18. A man can row across a lake $2\frac{1}{4}$ miles wide in 42 min. What is his average rate of rowing per hour?

19. A man finds that his automobile goes $86\frac{1}{4}$ miles on 5 gal of gasoline. How many gallons of gasoline would he expect to use on a 354-mile trip?

20. At $35 per acre what is the value of $87\frac{3}{4}$ acres of land?

21. Write in words the number 2086.354.

22. Write as a decimal the number twelve thousand four hundred sixty-seven and thirty-eight thousandths.

23. At $75 an acre how much will 62.4 acres of land cost?

24. Find the value of 48.6 tons of hay at $25.75 per ton.

25. A farmer has cotton planted on four separate plots of ground whose acreages are 34.6, 28.75, 0.8, and 19 acres. What is the total acreage planted in cotton?

26. If 4386 lb of lint are produced on 23.4 acres, what is the yield per acre, expressed to the nearest hundredth of a pound?

27. Express the following as exact decimal fractions: $\frac{3}{4}, \frac{1}{8}, \frac{3}{16}, \frac{4}{5}$.

28. Express the following as decimal fractions, to the nearest thousandth: $\frac{2}{3}$, $\frac{5}{6}$, $\frac{2}{7}$, $\frac{5}{9}$.

29. If the lengths of the four sides of a field are 22.75, 17.65, 28.6, and 18.35 rods, what will the fence to inclose the field cost at $4.13 per rod?

30. If the posts for the fence mentioned in Problem 29 are placed not more than 12 ft apart, about how many posts will be required?

31. In a certain fertilizer for corn land 0.475 of the fertilizer is cotton-seed meal, 0.43 is phosphoric acid, and the rest is kainit. How many pounds of each are there in a ton of the fertilizer?

32. A sample of average milk is found to be 0.87 water (by weight). How many pounds of water are there in 10 gal of such milk?

33. A steer whose live weight was 560 lb dressed 308 lb. The dressed weight was what part of the live weight? Express the result as a decimal.

34. 1760 lb is what part of a ton? Express the result as a decimal.

35. A $12\frac{1}{2}$-lb strip of bacon was bought at 28¢ per pound and sold sliced, without rind, at 50¢ a pound. What was the profit if the weight of the rind was 0.16 of the weight of the strip?

36. A certain grain mixture for poultry consists of 150 lb of wheat, 200 lb of cracked corn, and 100 lb of oats. What part of this mixture is wheat? What part is cracked corn? What part is oats?

37. If barley is quoted at $1.40 per bushel, what is the value of a ton of barley?

38. If new ear corn is worth $38 per ton, what is the value per bushel?

39. If ear corn is worth $36 per ton on May 1 of a certain year, what should shelled corn be worth, neglecting shelling costs and value of cobs?

40. Which is the greater, one third of $18\frac{4}{7}$ or three times $2\frac{1}{14}$? How much greater?

41. If a steer whose dressed weight was 308 lb lost $\frac{9}{20}$ of its live weight in dressing, what was its live weight?

42. In one year $\frac{9}{20}$ of the usual cotton acreage on a certain farm was planted in other crops. If there were 78 acres left in cotton, what was the acreage usually planted in cotton on this farm?

43. In a certain field that is almost uniformly white with cotton, it is observed that the seed cotton picked from 4 rows weighs 120 lb. If the field measures 480 yd (crosswise to the rows) and the rows are 3 ft apart and of equal length, estimate the yield in bales from this picking of the field, counting 1500 lb of seed cotton to the bale.

44. In a certain 1600-lb bale of seed cotton (the remnant of the crop) the land owner, a tenant, and a cropper have interests as follows: The land owner has full interest in 300 lb, one-fourth interest in 400 lb, and half interest in 900 lb; the tenant has three-fourths interest in 400 lb;

and the cropper has half interest in 900 lb. If ginning yields 540 lb of lint that sells at 32¢ per pound and 1000 lb of seed that sells at $70 per ton, how should the receipts be divided among the three interested persons after $9 is deducted to cover ginning, storage, and insurance?

45. Light travels at approximately 186,330 miles per second. Find to the nearest second how long it takes light to travel from the sun to the earth, a distance of approximately 92,897,400 miles.

46. It is estimated that 700 lb of shelled corn will produce 100 lb of live-weight pork, and that 300 lb of shelled corn with 25 lb of tankage and 25 lb of cottonseed meal will produce 100 lb of live-weight pork. If shelled corn is worth $3.75 per hundredweight, tankage is worth $6 per hundredweight, and cottonseed meal is worth $3.80 per hundredweight, would it pay a farmer to trade some of his corn for tankage and cottonseed meal and feed the mixture? How much can he afford to pay for tankage to make this replacement of corn by tankage?

47. The following mixture of feeds makes 1000 lb of a standard baby chick ration: 300 lb ground yellow corn at $3.50 per hundredweight; 300 lb gray wheat shorts at $3.40 per hundredweight; 100 lb ground oats at $4.20 per hundredweight; 60 lb dried buttermilk at $7 per hundredweight; 60 lb meat scraps at $5.90 per hundredweight; 60 lb cottonseed meal at $3.80 per hundredweight; 50 lb alfalfa leaf meal at $4.60 per hundredweight; 20 lb finely ground oyster shell at $1.00 per hundredweight; 10 lb salt at $1.10 per hundredweight; 40 lb bran at $3.30 per hundredweight; 1 pt triple-strength cod liver oil at $2.40 per gallon. This same feed can be bought ready mixed at $5.50 per hundredweight. Disregarding the labor cost of mixing and also the difference in thoroughness of mixing, find how much a farmer saves per 100 lb by mixing the feed instead of buying it ready mixed.

48. A man employed on a dairy farm received for a year's work the following: $100 a month as wages, free house rent worth $35 per month, 365 gal of milk worth 72¢ per gallon, 52 lb of butter worth 70¢ per pound, and 12 bu of potatoes worth $2.75 per bushel. What he received was equivalent to what salary for the year?

49. What is the gross profit per quart on milk bought for 20¢ a quart and sold at 10¢ a glass, there being two glasses to a pint?

50. It is estimated that skim milk for feeding purposes is worth half as much per 100 lb as corn is worth per bushel. What should be the value of 160 lb of skim milk when corn is worth $1.40 per bushel?

51. On the basis of the comparison of feeding values mentioned in Problem 50, a pound of shelled corn is worth how many times as much as a pound of skim milk? The value of a pound of skim milk is what part of the value of a pound of shelled corn?

52. It is estimated that an 8-in. fan uses electric energy at the rate of

20 w* (that is, 20 whr of energy per hour). At 4¢ per kilowatt-hour what would be the cost of running this fan 8 hr each day for 26 days?

53. At 3¢ per kilowatt-hour what should it cost to operate a 6-lb 550-w flat iron for 40 hr?

54. A certain city has the following rates for electric power: First 20 kwhr at 10¢, with a minimum charge of $2 per month; next 30 kwhr at 5¢; next 50 kwhr at 4¢; next 200 kwhr at 3¢; and all in excess of 300 kwhr at 2¢ per kilowatthour. Find the amount of the bill for each of the following monthly consumptions of electric energy: (a) 18 kwhr, (b) 35 kwhr, (c) 70 kwhr, (d) 210 kwhr, (e) 450 kwhr.

55. The following estimates were made of the electric energy required each month for a certain home: Lighting, 25 kwhr; iron 6 kwhr; refrigerator, 50 kwhr; radio, 10 kwhr. Using the rates given in Problem 54, calculate the amount of the bill for the month.

56. Using the rates given in Problem 54, calculate the amount of the monthly bill for electric energy used in a home with the following estimated requirements:

Appliance	Number of Appliances	Watts per Hour Used by Appliance	Hours Used per Day	Days Used per Month
Lamp	1	25	2	30
Lamp	3	60	4	30
Lamp	2	75	3	30
Lamp	1	100	2	30
Iron	1	500	6	4
Washing machine	1	200	3	4
Refrigerator	1	250	8	30
Radio	1	150	6	30

57. Using the rates given in Problem 54, make an estimate of the cost per month of lighting a 5-room house, listing the requirements for each room.

58. At 3¢ per kilowatt-hour, what would be the cost of brooder operation for 1000 baby chicks for a period of 6 weeks if 100 whr were required per chick per week?

59. It is estimated that 15 kwhr of electric energy are required for incubating 100 eggs. At 3½¢ per kilowatt-hour find the cost of energy required to incubate 1200 eggs.

---

* The unit of electric energy is the watt-hour (whr). A kilowatt-hour (kwhr) is 1000 whr and is the unit that most electric meters register and upon which rates for electricity are usually based. Lamps and other electric appliances usually bear markings that indicate the number of watt-hours used per hour. Thus a lamp marked 75 w uses 75 whr of energy in 1 hr.

60. If three-quarters of the 1200 eggs placed in an incubator are expected to hatch, and a chick requires $\frac{1}{2}$ kwhr during the brooding period, estimate the expected brooding cost for this lot of chicks, assuming that the average number present in the brooder is 0.95 of the number hatched and that $3\frac{1}{2}\cent$ per kilowatt-hour is to be paid for electricity.

61. If a corn sheller consumes 7 kwhr of electricity per 100 bushels of corn shelled, find the cost at 2.75¢ per kilowatt-hour of shelling $4\frac{1}{2}$ tons of ear corn weighing 70 lb per bushel.

62. At $0.025 per kilowatt-hour, find the cost of grinding 1000 bu of ear corn (husk and cob included) weighing 72 lb per bushel, if the grinder consumes $1\frac{1}{4}$ kwhr of energy per 100 lb of feed ground.

63. If 2 kwhr of energy are consumed by an electrically driven pump in lifting to a height of 10 ft enough water to provide an acre with a 1-in. coverage of water, find the cost of lifting to this height enough water to supply a $2\frac{1}{2}$-in. coverage to a 60-acre field, the cost rate being 3¢ per kilowatt-hour.

64. It is estimated that operating milking machines requires 20 kwhr of electric energy per month for each 10 cows. At 2¢ per kilowatt-hour, estimate the cost of energy consumed in a year by milking machines on a dairy that maintains an average of 40 producing cows.

65. If 6 kwhr of electricity are used per day in sterilizing dairy utensils for each 25 cows milked, find at 3¢ per kilowatt-hour the monthly cost of this operation on a 40-cow dairy.

66. Consider that an electrically driven cream separator requires about $\frac{1}{2}$ kwhr of energy per 1000 lb of milk processed by it. At 3¢ per kilowatt-hour, find the monthly cost of energy for this operation on a farm where an average of 840 lb of milk is run through the separator each day.

67. A 150-ft roll of 60-in. poultry fencing of a certain brand weighs about 46.8 lb. Estimate the total number of feet of fencing contained in 4 partially used rolls weighing 23 lb, $11\frac{1}{2}$ lb, 8 lb, and $17\frac{3}{4}$ lb.

68. A Leghorn laying hen requires about 35 lb of mash and 50 lb of grain per year. With mash costing $4.60 per hundredweight and grain costing $4.00 per hundredweight, how many eggs worth 40¢ per dozen must a hen lay in a year to pay only her feed bill?

69. Using the data given in Problem 68, estimate the profit above feed and labor costs to be expected from a flock of 1000 hens averaging 200 eggs each per year if the total labor cost is reckoned at $3.00 per day including Sundays?

70. Using the data of Problem 68 and estimating the labor cost to be $\frac{1}{4}$ as much as the feed cost, what should be the average annual production of eggs per hen in order for a flock of 1000 birds to yield their owner a gross profit equal to one-quarter of his investment in feed and labor?

71. In a daily ration for ewes, consisting of $3\frac{1}{2}$ lb alfalfa and 2 lb corn silage, what part of the ration is alfalfa?

72. Another ration for ewes consists of 2 lb oat straw, 2 lb corn silage, ¾ lb shelled corn, and ¼ lb linseed meal. The shelled corn makes up what part of the ration?

73. A cotton-picking machine costing $6800.00 and expected to have 8 years of usefulness should be worth about how much at the end of 5 years if the amount of depreciation annually is considered constant? Its value then is what part of the purchase price?

74. Estimating that a mechanical picker can harvest 8 bales of cotton in a 10-hour day at an average cost of $12.00 per bale, find approximately the per-hour cost of operating the picker.

75. Suppose that at prevailing cotton prices during a certain harvesting season hand-picked cotton brings about 2¢ per pound of lint more than machine-picked cotton from the same field. With hand-picking costs at $30.00 per bale and machine-picking costs at $12.00 per bale, which is the more economical method of harvesting? What gain is realized by the one method over the other in harvesting a crop of 180 bales? (500 lb lint per bale.)

76. A mechanical cotton picker costing $8829 may be expected to render satisfactory service for 6 years, picking an average of 200 bales per season. On two occasions during this period it is likely that 600 spindles will have to be replaced at a cost of $2.75 each. Other necessary repair costs will average about $200 per year. Estimating fuel and lubrication costs at $1.50 and labor costs at $2.50 per bale, service value rendered by the machine at $24.00 per bale, and value of tractor part of machine at end of 6-year period at $1000, find the approximate net return made by the machine to its owner for the 6-yr period.

77. In some areas where high winds are prevalent, storm-resistant varieties of cotton are planted and machine harvesting is done by a "stripper" which removes practically all the cotton bolls from the field in one operation. If it is estimated that machine stripping costs $25 per bale while hand pulling of the bolls costs $2.00 per hundred pounds, how many 2000-pound bales must a stripper harvest in order for the saving over hand pulling to pay for the stripper costing $1050?

78. If use of the stripper mentioned in Problem 77 results in a saving of $15 per bale in harvesting cost, along with a loss of 1½¢ per pound of lint due to lowering of grade, estimate the net saving to be expected by the owner throughout an 8-year life of a stripper in which its average annual harvest is 120 bales.

79. In a 10-hour day a jeep pulling a 2-section harrow travels 30 miles in harrowing a 25-acre field and consumes 3.75 gal of gasoline costing 24¢ per gallon. Find (a) the number of acres harrowed per hour, (b) the rate of travel in miles per hour, (c) the number of miles traveled per gallon of fuel, (d) the number of gallons of fuel required per acre, and (e) the fuel cost per acre.

CHAPTER 2

PERCENTAGE

Meaning of Per Cent

The phrase *per cent* is a contraction of the Latin *per centum*, which means *by the hundred* or *for each one hundred*. It is used in mathematics as having exactly the same meaning as the word *hundredths*. The phrase *5 per cent* means *5 hundredths*, and may be written as 0.05, $\frac{5}{100}$, or $\frac{1}{20}$. The symbol % is read "per cent." By expressing rates in a common "per hundred" form, per cents provide a convenient and standard basis for comparing rates.

Problems Involving Per Cents

A percentage problem usually involves three numbers, the *base*, the *rate*, and the *percentage* related in this way:

$$\text{Rate} \times \text{base} = \text{percentage}$$

The identity of each of these terms may be observed from the statement that
$$8\% \text{ of } 365 = 0.08 \times 365 = 29.20,$$
in which 8% or 0.08 is the *rate*, 365 is the *base*, and 29.20 is the *percentage*.* Since a problem may require finding any one of these elements from a knowledge of the other two, there are three main types of problems involving per cents. The following may help the student to recognize these types of problems and to understand the principles and methods used in solving them.

    1. PROBLEM: Finding a per cent of a number.
      Form of relation: Percentage = rate × base.
      Example: Find 12.5% of 368.
$$12.5\% \text{ of } 368 = 0.125 \times 368 = 46.000$$
      or $12.5\% \text{ of } 368 = \frac{1}{8} \times 368 = 46.$

---

  * The word *percentage* is also used in a broader sense to mean the whole subject matter dealing with computations involving per cents.

2. **PROBLEM:** Finding a number of which a per cent is known.

   Form of relation: Base = percentage ÷ rate.

   Example: $155 is 40% of what amount?

   $$155 \div 0.40 = 387.50$$

   or $\quad 155 \div \tfrac{2}{5} = 155 \times \tfrac{5}{2} = 387.50.$

   $155 is 40% of $387.50.

3. **PROBLEM:** Finding what per cent one number is of another.

   Form of relation: Rate = percentage ÷ base.

   Example: 243 acres is what per cent of 682 acres?

   243 is $\tfrac{243}{682}$ of 682.

   $\tfrac{243}{682} = 0.3563$ approximately.

   $\quad\quad = 35.6$ approximately.

Hence, 243 acres is approximately 35.6% of 682 acres.

Per Cent Equivalents

Every per cent is equivalent to a common fraction and may be replaced by it in making computations. Thus

$$37\tfrac{1}{2}\% = \frac{37\tfrac{1}{2}}{100} = \tfrac{3}{8}.$$

The student will find it well worth while to memorize the following table of per cents and equivalent common fractions:

$25\% = \tfrac{1}{4}$	$20\% = \tfrac{1}{5}$	$10\% = \tfrac{1}{10}$	$12\tfrac{1}{2}\% = \tfrac{1}{8}$	$8\tfrac{1}{3}\% = \tfrac{1}{12}$
$50\% = \tfrac{1}{2}$	$40\% = \tfrac{2}{5}$	$30\% = \tfrac{3}{10}$	$37\tfrac{1}{2}\% = \tfrac{3}{8}$	$16\tfrac{2}{3}\% = \tfrac{1}{6}$
$75\% = \tfrac{3}{4}$	$60\% = \tfrac{3}{5}$	$70\% = \tfrac{7}{10}$	$62\tfrac{1}{2}\% = \tfrac{5}{8}$	$33\tfrac{1}{3}\% = \tfrac{1}{3}$
$100\% = 1$	$80\% = \tfrac{4}{5}$	$90\% = \tfrac{9}{10}$	$87\tfrac{1}{2}\% = \tfrac{7}{8}$	$66\tfrac{2}{3}\% = \tfrac{2}{3}$

Per cents may be replaced by equivalent decimal numbers simply by moving the decimal point two places to the left (thus, dividing by 100) and leaving off the per cent symbol. For example,

$$8.75\% = 0.0875.$$

The following examples illustrate certain applications of percentage.

Examples

1. Find the interest on $300 at 8% for 3 months.

Interest, in its simplest form, may be considered as the rent paid for the use of money. The problem as stated implies that the interest to be paid by the borrower is to be computed on the basis of 8% of $300 for *one year's* use of the money.

8% of 300 = 0.08 × 300 = 24.00.

The interest for 1 year would be $24.00.

3 months is $\frac{3}{12}$ or $\frac{1}{4}$ of a year.

$\frac{1}{4}$ of 24.00 = 6.00.

Hence the required interest is $6.00.

2. If a salesman receives for his services a commission amounting to 5% of his sales, what total sales in a year would render him a gross income of $7000?

Evidently, this is equivalent to asking the question, "$7000 is 5% of what amount?" and the solution employs the relation:

Base = percentage ÷ rate

Base = 7000 ÷ 0.05

= 140,000

Conclusion: $140,000 = total sales required.

3. A 5-year-old tractor, costing $1875 when new and worth about $750, now may be considered as having suffered what average annual per cent of depreciation?

$1875 − $750 = $1125 = depreciation for 5-year period

$1125 ÷ 5   = $225 = average annual depreciation

The problem is now resolved into the settlement of this question, "$225 is what per cent of $1875?" Using the relation:

Rate = percentage ÷ base,

we have   Rate = 225 ÷ 1875

= 0.12

Conclusion: The average annual per cent of depreciation of the tractor is 12%.

Problems

1. How many acres is 35% of 256 acres?

2. An inch is what per cent of a foot?

3. The most valuable constituent of milk is butterfat. How many pounds of butterfat are there in 15 gal of milk testing 4.5% butter fat?

4. Calves lose about 40% of their live weight in dressing. Find approximately what the dressed weight of a 230-lb calf should be.

5. A farmer decreased his wheat acreage of 80 acres by 15%. How many acres did he then have in wheat?

6. A farmer has 72 acres of land in cotton, and this is 45% of his entire farm. How many acres are there in his farm?

7. A man bought a piece of land for $4500 and sold it so as to gain 8% of what it cost him. How much did he gain and what was the selling price?

8. In conducting a germination test on seed corn a farmer found that 108 grains out of 150 germinated. What per cent germinated?

9. Of 350 eggs placed in an incubator 243 hatched. What per cent of the eggs hatched?

10. How much interest does a man pay on $300 borrowed for 8 months at $7\frac{1}{2}$% per annum?

11. What is the cash cost of 18 spools of barb wire at $6.80, subject to discounts of 10% and 2%? (It is understood that the second discount is on the remainder resulting from the first discount.)

12. How many gallons of milk testing 4.8% are required to produce 36 lb of butterfat?

13. In making ice cream the volume of the unfrozen mixture may be increased 80% by whipping. How many gallons of mixture would be required to make 10 gal of ice cream?

14. A farmer budded 265 pecan trees, one bud to a tree, and found that 171 buds lived. What per cent of the buds lived?

15. Nico-dust, which is used to kill lice on melons, is made by mixing "Black-Leaf 40" with lime. How much "Black-Leaf 40" would be used with 25 lb of lime to make a dust testing 2% "Black-Leaf 40"?

16. The composition of average shelled corn is as follows: protein, 10.1%; fat, 5.0%; ash, 1.5%; carbohydrates, 72.9%; and water, 10.5%. How many pounds of each of these are there in a bushel of average corn?

17. A feeder gets a bill for $800 due in 60 days with 2% off for cash. Would it pay him to borrow money from the bank at 8% per annum in order to take advantage of the cash discount?

18. The top $6\frac{2}{3}$ in. of soil, called the "top soil," is usually considered as weighing 2,000,000 lb to the acre. If a sample of top soil from a certain field is found to be 0.15% nitrogen by weight, how many pounds of nitrogen per acre are there in the top soil?

19. Average milk is composed (by weight) of 3.80% fat, 3.55% protein, 4.90% lactose, 0.71% ash, and water. What per cent is water? How many pounds of water are there in a gallon of average milk?

20. A sample of soil weighing 189 g lost 39 g when thoroughly dried in an electric oven at 110°C. What was the per cent of moisture in the sample?

21. A farmer borrowed $250 on Jan. 15 at 8%. What amount, principal and interest, should he pay on Oct. 15 of the same year?

22. A man bought 12 head of cattle on Feb. 1 at $45 a head, promising to pay for them later with interest at 10%. If he paid the bill on the following Apr. 16, how much did he pay?

23. On a note for $375 at 6% a payment of $30 is credited annually at the close of each year from its date for 3 yr. How much is due at the end of the fourth year?

24. A farmer borrows $300 from a bank for 6 months at 8%. If the bank collects the interest in advance, the farmer actually has the use of what sum of money for the 6 months? What rate of interest is the farmer actually paying?

25. A butcher bought a prime 400-lb steer at 24¢ per pound. The animal dressed 60%, and the average selling price of the meat per pound was $0.80. What was the total gross profit? What was the per cent of gross profit?

26. A farmer bought 600 baby chicks at 12¢ each. He lost 70 of them, and the average cost of raising the rest to an average weight of 2 lb was 24¢. If he sold them at 35¢ per pound, what were his earnings? His earnings were what per cent of his investment?

27. If a horse is worth $160 at the age of 3 yr but is worth only $24 at the age of 20 yr, what is the average annual depreciation? The average annual depreciation is what per cent of the value of the horse at the age of 3 yr?

28. A formula developed by the Minnesota Agricultural Experiment Station for the approximate annual depreciation, d, of milch cows is

$$d = 0.015V_o + 0.16\tfrac{2}{3}(V_o - V_n),$$

where V_o is the number of dollars in the original value, and V_n is the number of dollars in the final "block" value. (The factor 0.015, or $1\tfrac{1}{2}$%, is allowed for accidental death losses, and the $16\tfrac{2}{3}$% is based upon a 6-yr milking life.) Counting the "block" value of a $175 cow as $70, find the approximate annual depreciation.

29. The life of a farm wagon is estimated as 20 yr. If the annual depreciation is assumed to be constant throughout the 20 yr, what is the rate of annual depreciation?

30. What is the expected life of a grain binder which depreciates approximately $8\tfrac{1}{3}$% of its original value each year?

31. Commercial fertilizers contain nitrogen, phosphoric acid, and potash in various proportions for different crops and soils. A fertilizer labeled 2-8-4 contains (by weight) 2% nitrogen, 8% available phosphoric acid, and 4% soluble potash. How many pounds of each of these are there in a ton of fertilizer so labeled?

32. Nitrate of soda is often used in fertilizers to supply the nitrogen. How many pounds of nitrate of soda testing 16% nitrogen would be required to furnish the 40 lb of nitrogen indicated in Problem 31?

33. Phosphates may be used in fertilizers to provide the phosphoric acid needed. How much superphosphate yielding 20% phosphoric acid is required to provide the 160 lb of phosphoric acid required in Problem 31?

34. Muriate of potash is a main source of potash in fertilizers. How many pounds of muriate of potash testing 50% potash are needed to supply the 80 lb of potash indicated in Problem 31?

35. In Problems 32, 33, and 34 we have determined the number of pounds of essential materials, or plant food carriers (250 lb of nitrate of soda, 800 lb of superphosphate, and 160 lb of muriate of potash), required to make the 2-8-4 fertilizer mentioned in Problem 31. Note that the sum of the weights of these carriers falls short of being a ton by 790 lb. Filler, usually in the form of sand or dry clay, is used to fill out the ton, thus making the fertilizer contain the proper per cents, 2-8-4, of nitrogen, phosphoric acid, and potash, respectively. Addition of filler also makes possible a more even distribution of the fertilizer. What per cent of the ton of fertilizer mentioned above is filler?

36. Practically the only plant foods contained in the fertilizer of Problem 31 are nitrogen, phosphoric acid, and potash. What per cent of the ton of fertilizer is plant food? What per cent is not plant food?

37. Compute the number of pounds of nitrogen, phosphoric acid, and potash in a ton of 4-8-4 fertilizer.

38. Find the number of pounds each of Chilean nitrate of soda testing 15% nitrogen, acid phosphate testing 16% phosphoric acid, and sulfate of potash testing 45% potash required to make the fertilizer mentioned in Problem 37.

39. How many pounds of filler are needed in the fertilizer mentioned in Problem 37? This filler makes up what per cent of the fertilizer?

40. What per cent of the fertilizer mentioned in Problem 37 is plant food? How many pounds of non-plant-food material are there in this ton of fertilizer?

41. Suppose that a farmer can buy the fertilizer mentioned in Problem 37 already mixed at $2.10 per hundredweight, and can buy the nitrate of soda at 3¢ per pound, the acid phosphate at 1½¢ per pound, and the sulfate of potash at 2½¢ per pound. Allowing for a 2% loss in mixing, and disregarding the cost of the labor of mixing, is it more economical for the farmer to buy the ready-mixed fertilizer or to buy the materials and mix them?

42. How many pounds of ammonium sulfate are required to furnish the nitrogen in 1200 lb of 3-8-4 fertilizer?

43. How many pounds of phosphate of lime are required to supply the phosphoric acid in 1800 lb of 4-10-0 fertilizer?

Determine the per cent of nitrogen, per cent of phosphoric acid, and per cent of potash in each of the following fertilizer mixtures. Table VI gives the composition of certain commonly used fertilizer materials.

44. 1200 lb of superphosphate (18%) and 800 lb of cottonseed meal.

45. 1200 lb of superphosphate (20%), 60 lb of cottonseed meal, and 200 lb of nitrate of soda.

46. 1080 lb of acid phosphate, 800 lb of cottonseed meal, and 120 lb of muriate of potash.

47. 800 lb of superphosphate (18%), 800 lb of cottonseed meal, 200 lb of nitrate of soda, and 200 lb of muriate of potash.

48. How many pounds each of nitrate of soda testing 16% nitrogen, superphosphate containing 18% phosphoric acid, and muriate of potash testing 50% potash are required for a ton of 5-10-5 fertilizer?

49. Barnyard manure contains about 0.6% nitrogen, 0.4% phosphoric acid, and 0.6% potash. If nitrogen is worth 15¢ per pound, phosphoric acid is worth 6¢ per pound, and potash is worth 5¢ per pound, what is the value of the plant food contained in a ton of manure?

50. What is the value of the plant food in the manure for a year from 125 head of sheep which weigh 80 lb each and produce 34 lb of manure per day per 1000 lb of live weight, if sheep manure tests 0.6% nitrogen, 0.3% phosphoric acid, and 0.55% potash and these plant foods are worth 12¢, 6¢, and 5¢ per pound, respectively?

51. The constituents of feeds, as indicated by most feed analyses, are (1) proteins, (2) ether extracts (consisting mainly of fats and oils), (3) nitrogen-free extract (consisting mainly of carbohydrates such as sugars and starches), (4) crude fiber (consisting chiefly of the cell walls and woody material of plants), (5) ash, which is the residue obtained when the feed is burned, and (6) water. Table VIII, page 188, gives the average composition of certain feeding stuffs. If corn contains 10.4% crude protein, while only 6.4% of corn is digestible protein, what per cent of corn is indigestible protein? What per cent of the crude protein is indigestible?

52. By reference to Problem 51, determine how many pounds of digestible protein are contained in a bushel of shelled corn.

53. How many pounds of protein are there in this feed mixture for brood sows: corn (shelled), 75 lb; wheat gray shorts, 13 lb; cottonseed meal, 7 lb; and tankage, 5 lb? What is the per cent of protein in this mixture?

Determine the per cent of protein in each of the following mixtures for dairy cattle:

54. 200 lb of corn meal, 100 lb of wheat bran, and 200 lb of cottonseed meal.

55. 400 lb of corn meal, 300 lb of cottonseed meal, 100 lb of ground oats, and 200 lb of wheat bran.

56. 400 lb of cottonseed, 200 lb of alfalfa meal, and 100 lb of wheat bran.

57. 100 lb of ground oats, 200 lb of dried beet pulp, 100 lb of molasses, 100 lb of wheat bran, and 300 lb of cottonseed meal.

58. If the minimum weight upon which freight charges are made for a carload of hogs is 16,500 lb, the freight rate from College Station to Fort Worth is 40¢ per hundredweight, the commission for marketing a carload of hogs is $18, and a miscellaneous charge of $24 is made to cover feed, yardage, insurance, and so forth, what is the cost of marketing at Fort Worth a carload (of minimum weight) of hogs from College Station? If there is a shrinkage of $3\frac{1}{2}\%$ in the weight of the hogs due to shipping, and the hogs are sold at $16.50 per hundredweight, what is the net amount received by the shipper?

59. Find the cost of marketing a carload of cattle weighing 22,000 lb, assuming a freight rate of 38¢ per hundredweight, a commission charge of 12¢ per hundredweight, a miscellaneous charge covering yardage, insurance, and so forth, of 10¢ per hundredweight, and a feed charge of 4¢ per hundredweight. If there is a shrinkage of 5% in live weight, and the cattle are sold at $22.50 per hundredweight, what is the net amount received by the shipper for the cattle?

60. At large slaughtering plants, the dressed weight of an animal is taken to mean the weight of the carcass after 48 hr of chilling. Actually, however, the warm carcass is weighed immediately after cleaning, and a reduction of 2% of the warm weight is allowed for loss in weight that will result from dripping and evaporation while chilling. If the live weight of a calf is 380 lb and the warm carcass weighs 228 lb, the dressed weight is what per cent of the live weight?

61. The slope of land is an important factor affecting soil losses due to flow of water over the land. Slope, when expressed as a per cent, is usually taken to mean the number of feet of fall in elevation per 100 ft of horizontal distance. If two points 100 ft apart (horizontal distance) differ in elevation by 8.1 ft, what is the per cent of slope of land between the two points?

62. Two points 240 ft apart (horizontal distance) differ in elevation by 15 ft. What is the slope, expressed as a per cent?

63. On a certain tract of land having a 3% slope the vertical interval between two terraces is $2\frac{1}{2}$ ft. How far apart horizontally are the terraces?

64. If an 1800-lb bale of pulled cotton (burr included) yields 550 lb of lint and 920 lb of seed, the seed cotton may be considered as yielding what per cent lint cotton?

65. A cubic foot of water at 4°C weighs about 62.4 lb, and a cubic foot of ice weighs about 57 lb. What volume of water at 4°C is required for conversion into 1 cu ft of ice? As a given quantity of water changes from the liquid state to ice what is the per cent of increase in its volume?

66. On the basis of the following estimates of receipts and expenses. find an approximate net annual income per ewe: annual lamb crop is about 120% of the number of ewes; lambs weighing about 65 lb are sold at 20¢ per pound; a ewe yields annually about 8 lb of wool worth 60¢ per pound; feed and pasture costs for the flock run about $12 per ewe.

67. Considering nitrogen as worth 15¢ per pound, available phosphoric acid 5¢ per pound, and water-soluble potash 5¢ per pound, compute the value of a ton of 2-8-4 fertilizer.

68. Using the values of fertilizer constituents stated in the preceding problem, compare the per-ton values of a 5-10-5 fertilizer and a 4-12-4 fertilizer.

69. What is the cost per pound of nitrogen if ammonium nitrate testing 33% nitrogen is bought at $81.50 per ton?

70. Determine the per cent of protein in a laying mash consisting of the following: 20 lb ground yellow corn, 14.75 lb wheat bran, 20 lb wheat shorts, 15 lb pulverized oats, 7 lb meat scrap, 5 lb alfalfa leaf meal, 15.5 lb soybean oil meal, 2 lb oyster shell, 0.5 lb salt, and 0.25 lb cod liver oil.

71. A summary of a farmer's business for a certain year shows: inventory at beginning of year $21,385.00, inventory at end of year $18,460.40, total receipts $15,079.75, total expenses $6382.72. Considering capital invested as having earning power amounting to 5% of the average inventory, how much may the farmer consider that he has earned by his own labor and management?

72. A farm valued at $16,000 rents for $2500 a year. Find the per cent return on investment realized by the owner if he pays out during the year $120.80 for taxes, $280.50 for repairs, and $48.30 for insurance.

73. Three mechanical cotton pickers costing $7820 each are estimated to have a season's rental value of 15% of their cost. Suppose that during a certain season the three machines pick 550 bales of cotton and that the following expenses of operation are incurred: fuel and lubrication $648.75, labor $1420.96, and repairs $134.50. Find the picking cost per bale.

74. If the owner of the three pickers mentioned in Problem 73 receives $2.00 per 100 lb of seed cotton for custom picking, how many 1500-lb bales must he harvest in order to recover, as net income over the operating costs specified, his original investment in the machines?

75. Under some conditions machine-picked cotton may be expected to bring about 2¢ per pound less than cotton picked by hand from the same field, and it is sometimes estimated that hand pickers will gather 1½% more cotton from a field than will be picked by machines. Considering these two factors and counting hand-picking costs at $24 per bale and machine-picking at $12 per bale, how much more might a producer have realized from hand-picking a field that yielded 1000 machine-picked bales (500 lb) that sold at an average price of 35¢ per pound, assuming that for each bale of cotton harvested there are 1000 lb of seed worth $72.00 per ton?

76. Two brothers, A and B, have interests of $\frac{1}{3}$ and $\frac{2}{3}$, respectively, in a $14,000 cotton harvesting machine. For custom picking during a season the machine and its crew earn $8280 for harvesting 460 bales. As machine operator and crew manager, A is allowed $20 per day for the 86 days of work required and pays out $1445 for labor, $759.60 for fuel and lubricants, and $347.85 for repairs. How much should B receive as his share of the net earnings of the machine for that season?

77. Assuming that the mechanical harvester of Problem 76 has depreciated 15% of its preseason value by the end of the season, what should be considered as the rate of earning on the investment in the machine? (Consider the period of investment, earning, and depreciation as a year.)

78. How many pounds of a 5-10-5 fertilizer should be applied per acre in order to provide each acre with 30 lb of nitrogen?

79. How many pounds of 4-8-4 fertilizer should be applied per acre to be equivalent to an application of 600 lb of 5-10-5 fertilizer?

80. Table VII gives information about the quantities of main plant food nutrients contained in good acre yields of certain crops. What per cent each of the nitrogen, the phosphoric acid, and the potash contained in the whole cotton plant is returned to the soil by turning under the burrs, leaves, and stalks? What per cent of the total of these nutrients is thus returned to the soil?

81. Application of 400 lb of 5-10-5 fertilizer to an acre of cotton land replenishes the soil with what per cent of each of the plant food nutrients removed in the yield of lint and seed shown in Table VII?

82. What per cent of the total plant food contained in the yield from 0.5 acre of potatoes, 0.3 acre of tomatoes, and 1.5 acres of sweet potatoes, as indicated in Table VII, is lost by removing the vines from the soil?

83. Assuming that burning organic matter on a field removes from the soil the nitrogen and phosphoric acid contained in the organic matter, how many pounds each of nitrogen and phosphoric acid are lost by burning the corn stalks and leaves from a 40-acre corn field, the yield per acre being 60 bu of grain? (See Table VII.) What per cent of the total of these two nutrients contained in the whole crop would be returned to the soil if this corn stover were turned under?

84. Application of 350 lb of 4-12-8 fertilizer to an acre of corn land replenishes the soil with what per cent of the total plant food nutrients removed in the yield of grain shown in Table VII?

CHAPTER 3

EQUATIONS

Meaning of an Equation

In solving problems, it is sometimes convenient to use a letter to stand for a number whose value is to be determined. After introducing a letter to represent an unknown number, a statement of equality may be written in which this letter is used just as the number it represents might be used if it were known. For example, consider the problem of finding the number of pounds of lint cotton that may be expected from 1260 lb of clean seed cotton, assuming that the weight of the seed is twice the weight of the lint. We may let n stand for the number of pounds of lint. Then $2n$ stands for the number of pounds of seed, and we may write the relation

$$n + 2n = 1260,$$

or

$$3n = 1260,$$

from which

$$n = 420.$$

Therefore we conclude that the 1260 lb of seed cotton would produce about 420 lb of lint.

A statement of equality between two number expressions is called an *equation*. The two expressions on opposite sides of the "is equal to" symbol are called the *members*, or the *sides*, of the equation. In the above problem, the statement that $n + 2n = 1260$ is an equation and may be considered as involving the letter n in such a way as to make it serve as the number it represents. Furthermore, if we substitute 420 for n in the equation above, we have

$$420 + 2(420) = 1260,$$

or

$$420 + 840 = 1260,$$

or

$$1260 = 1260.$$

25

Thus the two members of the equation become exactly the same when the proper value is substituted for n. This value of n (that is, 420) is said to *satisfy* the equation. Also, 420 is called a *root* of the equation.

Solving Equations

The process of finding the value of an unknown in an equation is called *solving the equation*. In solving an equation any changes may be made that do not destroy the equality of the members of the equation. The following operations are the main ones used in solving an equation, and each of these operations results in a new equation whose two sides are equal.

1. *Addition of the same number to each side.*
2. *Subtraction of the same number from each side.*
3. *Multiplication of each side by the same number.*
4. *Division of each side by the same number (not zero).*

Each of the equations obtained by performing one of the above operations imposes on the letter representing the unknown number the same value as is imposed by the original equation. By making successive changes in the form of an equation we try to arrive at an equation of the form

$$x = \text{a certain number,}$$

which gives directly the information sought.

Negative Numbers

Since solving equations frequently involves handling numbers not dealt with in arithmetic, it may be well to remind the student that algebra involves not only the *positive* numbers and zero used in arithmetic, but also a set of so-called *negative* numbers. Corresponding to every positive number there is a number of *equal magnitude* which has a "minus" sign associated with it and which is regarded as being exactly as far *below zero* in our number system as the corresponding positive number is *above zero*. Thus, corresponding to $+6$ (or simply, 6) which is considered as being 6 units *above 0* there is the negative number -6 (read "minus six") which is considered as being 6 units *below 0*. The distinctive natures of these two numbers, as thus prescribed, are such that if they are combined by addition the result is 0, and if their difference is determined as the number of units that the $+6$ is *above* the -6 in our number system, that difference is 12. We say, in this connection that $+6$ *exceeds* -6 by 12. Thus

$$(+6) + (-6) = 0 \quad \text{and} \quad (+6) - (-6) = 12.$$

Note that adding (-6) to $(+6)$ is equivalent to subtracting $(+6)$ from $(+6)$ and that subtracting (-6) from $(+6)$ is equivalent to adding $(+6)$ to $(+6)$.

The *absolute* (or numerical) value of a number is the *magnitude* of the number and is positive, regardless of the sign of the number. Thus the absolute value of $+6$, indicated by $|+6|$, is 6, and the absolute value of -6, $|-6|$, is also 6.

While manipulative skill in handling signed numbers can be acquired only through practice, mastery of the following principles should prepare the student for proceeding with such practice.

Addition

1. In adding two numbers having like signs, add their absolute values and prefix their common sign.

Example

$$5 + 8 = 13; \qquad (-5) + (-8) = -13.$$

2. In adding two numbers having opposite signs, obtain the difference between their absolute values and prefix the sign of the one having the greater magnitude.

Example

$$(-8) + (+5) = -3; \qquad (+8) + (-5) = 3.$$

Subtraction

The following two principles make it possible to replace the subtraction of a signed number by an equivalent addition.

1. Subtracting a positive number is equivalent to adding a negative number of the same magnitude.

Examples

$$(+5) - (+8) = +5 + (-8) = -3.$$
$$(-5) + (+8) = -5 + (-8) = -13.$$

2. Subtracting a negative number is equivalent to adding a positive number of the same magnitude.

Examples

$$(+5) - (-8) = (+5) + (+8) = 13.$$
$$(-5) - (-8) = (-5) + (+8) = 3.$$
$$(+8) - (-5) = (+8) + (+5) = 13.$$
$$(-8) - (-5) = (-8) + (+5) = -3.$$

Multiplication

1. The product of two signed numbers is the product of their absolute values prefixed by a *plus sign* if the numbers have *like signs* and prefixed by a *minus sign* if the numbers have *unlike signs*.

Examples

$$(+8)(+5) = 40; \qquad (-8)(-5) = 40.$$
$$(+8)(-5) = -40; \qquad (-8)(+5) = -40.$$

2. A product of several signed numbers is *positive* if there is an *even number* of *negative factors*, and is *negative* if there is an *odd number* of *negative factors*.

Examples

$$(-3)(+5)(-8) = 120.$$
$$(+2)(-1)(-3)(-4)(+5)(-6) = 720.$$
$$(+5)(-3)(+8) = -120.$$
$$(-5)(-3)(+8)(-2) = -240.$$

Division

In dividing one signed number by another, operate with their absolute values prefixing to the result a *plus sign* if the numbers have *like signs* and prefixing a *negative sign* if the numbers have *unlike signs*.

Examples

$$(+40) \div (+8) = 5; \qquad (-40) \div (-8) = 5.$$
$$(+40) \div (-8) = -5; \qquad (-40) \div (+8) = -5.$$
$$(+8) \div (-40) = \frac{+8}{-40} = -\frac{1}{5}.$$
$$(-8) \div (-40) = \frac{-8}{-40} = \frac{1}{5}.$$

Parentheses

Parentheses ( ), brackets [ ], and braces { } are frequently used in grouping terms to show precisely the manner and order in which operations are to be performed. A sign applied to a parenthesis (or other symbol of grouping) may be considered either as affecting each term as it is removed from within the parenthesis or as affecting the result of operations indicated within the parenthesis. Consequently, *a parenthesis preceded by a plus sign may be removed without changing signs of terms enclosed; while removal of a parenthesis preceded by a minus sign must be accompanied by a change in the sign of every term enclosed.*

Examples

1. $9 + (7 - 2) = 9 + 7 - 2 = 14$

  or $\quad\quad\quad = 9 + 5 \quad\quad = 14.$

2. $13 - (4 + 7) = 13 - 4 + 7 = 16$

  or $\quad\quad\quad = 13 - (-3) = 13 + 3 = 16.$

3. $5a - 9b + 2(a + 3b) = 5a - 9b + 2a - 6b = 7a - 15b.$

4. $3x^2 - 8xy - 5x(2x + 4y) = 3x^2 - 8xy - 10x^2 + 20xy = -7x^2 + 12xy.$

5.* $7a + 2\{3a - 5[a - 2(1 - a)] - 8\}$

$\quad = 7a + 2\{3a - 5[a - 2 + 2a] - 8\}$

$\quad = 7a + 2\{3a - 5a + 10 - 10a - 8\}$

$\quad = 7a + 6a - 10a + 20 - 20a - 16.$

$\quad = -17a + 4.$

Preliminary Exercises

1. Add: (a) 15 (b) 15 (c) -15 (d) -15

          5 -5 5 -5

2. Subtract the lower number from the upper number

  (a) 15 (b) 15 (c) 5 (d) -5 (e) -5

     5 -5 15 15 -15

3. Do the multiplication indicated.

  (a) $15(5)$; (b) $15(-5)$; (c) $-15(5)$; (d) $(-15)(-5)$; (e) $-5(-15)$

4. Perform the division indicated.

  (a) $15 \div 5$; (b) $15 \div (-5)$; (c) $(-15) \div 5$; (d) $(-15) \div (-5)$;

  (e) $\dfrac{-15}{5}$; (f) $\dfrac{-5}{-15}$; (g) $\dfrac{-5}{15}$; (h) $\dfrac{-15}{-5}$

Simplify by removing signs of grouping and performing operations indicated.

5. $3a - 2[a + (5 - 2a)].$ **8.** $(a + 7b)(2a - 5b).$

6. $8 - 3(2 - 7) + 4(2 - 3).$ **9.** $(2x - 5y)[3x - (2x - y)].$

7. $10a^2 - 3a(2a + b) - 4b^2 + ab.$ **10.** $(15a^2 - 6ab + 3a) \div 3a.$

The student may find it helpful to verify the results obtained in the illustrative problems on the following page and to use that table as a reference on operations with numbers.

---

* In this case it is suggested that the signs of grouping be removed step by step, beginning with the innermost pair.

Addition	Subtraction	Multiplication	Division
$6 + 2 = 8$ $6 + (-2) = 4$ $(-6) + 2 = -4$ $(-6) + (-2) = -8$	$6 - 2 = 4$ $6 - (-2) = 8$ $(-6) - 2 = -8$ $(-6) - (-2) = -4$	$(6)(2) = 12$ $(6)(-2) = -12$ $(-6)(2) = -12$ $(-6)(-2) = 12$	$6 \div 2 = 3$ $6 \div (-2) = -3$ $(-6) \div 2 = -3$ $(-6) \div (-2) = 3$
$6a + 2a = 8a$ $6a + (-2a) = 4a$ $(-6a) + (2a) = -4a$ $(-6a) + (-2a) = -8a$	$6a - 2a = 4a$ $6a - (-2a) = 8a$ $(-6a) - (2a) = -8a$ $(-6a) - (-2a) = -4a$	$(6a)(2a) = 12a^2$ $(6a)(-2a) = -12a^2$ $(-6a)(2a) = -12a^2$ $(-6a)(-2a) = 12a^2$	$6a \div 2a = 3$ $6a \div (-2a) = -3$ $(-6a) \div 2a = -3$ $(-6a) \div (-2a) = 3$
$(3a) + (2b) = 3a + 2b$	$(3a) - (2b) = 3a - 2b$	$(3a)(2b) = 6ab$	$(3a) \div (2b) = \dfrac{3a}{2b}$
$(3a - 2b) + (a - 5b)$ $= 3a - 2b + a - 5b$ $= 4a - 7b$	$(3a - 2b) - (a - 5b)$ $= 3a - 2b - a + 5b$ $= 2a + 3b$	$(3a + 2b)(a - 5b)$ $= 3a^2 - 15ab + 2ab - 10b^2$ $= 3a^2 - 13ab - 10b^2$	$(3a - 2b) \div (a - 5b) = \dfrac{3a - 2b}{a - 5b}$
$(5a^2 - 3ab + b^2)$ $+ (2a^2 - 4b^2) + (a^2 - 2ab)$ $\begin{array}{l} 5a^2 - 3ab + b^2 \\ 2a^2 \quad\;\; - 4b^2 \\ a^2 - 2ab \\ \hline 8a^2 - 5ab - 3b^2 \end{array}$	$(5a^2 - 3ab - b^2)$ $- (2a^2 + 4ab - 3c)$ $\begin{array}{l} 5a^2 - 3ab - b^2 \\ 2a^2 + 4ab \quad\;\; - 3c \\ \hline 3a^2 - 7ab - b^2 + 3c \end{array}$	$(a^2 - 3ab - b^2)(5a + 2b)$ $\begin{array}{l} a^2 - 3ab - b^2 \\ 5a + 2b \\ \hline 5a^3 - 15a^2b - 5ab^2 \\ + 2a^2b - 6ab^2 - 2b^3 \\ \hline 5a^3 - 13a^2b - 11ab^2 - 2b^3 \end{array}$	$(8a^3 - 27b^3) \div (2a - 3b)$ $\begin{array}{r} 4a^2 + 6ab + 9b^2 \\ 2a - 3b \,\overline{)\,8a^3 \qquad\quad - 27b^3} \\ \underline{8a^3 - 12a^2b} \qquad\quad \\ 12a^2b \qquad - 27b^3 \\ \underline{12a^2b - 18ab^2} \qquad \\ 18ab^2 - 27b^3 \\ \underline{18ab^2 - 27b^3} \end{array}$

Examples

1. Solve $\frac{1}{2}x = 14 - \frac{1}{5}x$ for x.

Multiply each member by 10 to clear of fractions:
$$10(\tfrac{1}{2}x) = 10(14 - \tfrac{1}{5}x),$$
or
$$5x = 140 - 2x.$$
Add $2x$ to each side:
$$7x = 140.$$
Divide each side by 7:
$$x = 20.$$

2. Solve $0.07y + 0.05(1100 - y) = 59$ for y.

Perform the indicated multiplication:
$$0.07y + 55.00 - 0.05y = 59.$$

Subtract 55 from each member:
$$0.07y - 0.05y = 59 - 55.$$
Collect terms:
$$0.02y = 4.$$
Divide each member by 0.02:
$$y = 200.$$

3. Solve $\dfrac{1}{n-2} = \dfrac{3}{n-3}$ for n.

Multiply each side by $(n-2)(n-3)$ to clear of fractions:
$$(n-2)(n-3)\left(\frac{1}{n-2}\right) = (n-2)(n-3)\left(\frac{3}{n-3}\right),$$
or
$$n - 3 = 3(n - 2),$$
or
$$n - 3 = 3n - 6.$$

Add $3 - 3n$ to each member:
$$n - 3n = -6 + 3.$$
Collect terms:
$$-2n = -3.$$

Divide each side by (-2):
$$n = \frac{-3}{-2},$$
or
$$n = \tfrac{3}{2}.$$

Problems

Solve each of the following equations for the letter involved, indicating how each form of equation is obtained from the preceding form:

1. $3x - 4 = 2$.

2. $5x = 8 - 3x$.

3. $4y + 3 = 11$.

4. $2t - 5 = 7 - 4t$.

5. $7x + 3 = 4x + 9$.

6. $5x - 4 = 3x + 10$.

7. $4x - 5 = x - 2$.

8. $\dfrac{2w}{3} = 5$.

9. $\dfrac{10}{3x} = 5$.

10. $\dfrac{12}{x} = \dfrac{3}{2}$.

11. $7 = \dfrac{1}{t}$.

12. $\dfrac{5h}{2} - 6 = h$.

13. $\dfrac{x}{2} - 1 = \dfrac{5}{6}$.

14. $\dfrac{x}{2} + \dfrac{x}{3} - \dfrac{x}{4} = \dfrac{7}{2}$.

15. $\dfrac{x - 7}{2} = \dfrac{3}{4} + \dfrac{x - 1}{8}$.

16. $\dfrac{5y + 3}{6} - \dfrac{y + 9}{2} + 2 = 0$.

17. $\dfrac{3w - 2}{5} - \dfrac{w + 3}{7} = 1$.

18. $\dfrac{3y - 2}{y - 1} - 4 = 0$.

19. $\dfrac{8}{2x - 3} - \dfrac{2}{3} = 2$.

20. $\dfrac{11}{2y} - \dfrac{3}{y} = 5$.

21. $3(4x - 3) + 15 = 2(x - 8)$.

22. $16 + 4y - 4 = y + 12$.

23. $\dfrac{1}{5 - 2x} = \dfrac{2}{8x - 5}$.

24. $\dfrac{2w + 3}{11} + \dfrac{w - 1}{3} = 2$.

25. $\dfrac{17x - 5}{3} - \dfrac{10x + 2}{4} = \dfrac{5x + 7}{2} - 5$.

26. $0.04x = 0.1x + 2.4$.

27. $7m + 29 = 2m - 1$.

28. 50% of $(100 + n) = 47\frac{1}{2} + n$.

29. 2.5% of $600 + 30\%$ of $n = 3.5\%$ of $(600 + n)$. [This of course may be written as $0.025(600) + 0.30n = 0.035(600 + n)$.]

30. $4\left(2y - \dfrac{1}{2}\right) - 6\left(\dfrac{y}{2} - \dfrac{1}{3}\right) = 2$.

31. $\dfrac{3x}{4} - \dfrac{7x}{12} = \dfrac{11x}{36} - \dfrac{8x}{9} + \dfrac{3}{2}$.

32. $\dfrac{2(x + 1)}{3} - \dfrac{3(x + 2)}{4} = \dfrac{x + 1}{6}$.

33. $x - \left(3x - \dfrac{2x - 5}{10}\right) = \dfrac{1}{6}(2x - 57) - \dfrac{5}{3}$.

34. $3(5 - 6x) - 5\{x - 5[1 - 3(x - 5)]\} = 23$.

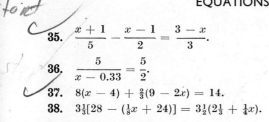

35. $\dfrac{x+1}{5} - \dfrac{x-1}{2} = \dfrac{3-x}{3}.$

36. $\dfrac{5}{x-0.33} = \dfrac{5}{2}.$

37. $8(x-4) + \tfrac{2}{3}(9-2x) = 14.$

38. $3\tfrac{1}{3}[28 - (\tfrac{1}{8}x + 24)] = 3\tfrac{1}{2}(2\tfrac{1}{3} + \tfrac{1}{4}x).$

Literal Equations

Many useful formulas are simply equations that involve several letters, each letter representing the measure of some concrete quantity. Such equations are called *literal equations*. A literal equation may be solved for any one of the letters involved by considering all the other letters as constants (numbers with fixed values), and using the methods employed in solving an equation containing only one letter.

Examples

1. The equation $I = Prt$ is the formula for finding the interest, I dollars, on a sum of money, P dollars, at rate r per year for t years.

To solve this equation for P, divide each side by rt:

$$P = \frac{I}{rt}.$$

To solve the equation for r, divide each side by Pt:

$$r = \frac{I}{Pt}.$$

2. $F = \tfrac{9}{5}C + 32$ is a formula expressing a temperature reading on the Fahrenheit scale in terms of a reading of the same temperature on the centigrade scale. Solving this equation for C gives the formula for changing a Fahrenheit reading to a centigrade reading.

$$F = \frac{9C}{5} + 32.$$

Multiply each member by 5:

$$5F = 9C + 160.$$

Subtract 160 from each side:

$$5F - 160 = 9C.$$

Divide each side by 9:

$$\frac{5F - 160}{9} = C.$$

Rewrite:

$$C = \frac{5F - 160}{9},$$

or

$$C = \tfrac{5}{9}(F - 32).$$

Problems

1. Solve $\dfrac{L_1}{L_2} = \dfrac{W_2}{W_1}$ for L_2.

2. Solve $C = 2\pi r$ for r.

3. Solve $A = P + Prt$ for P.

4. Solve $S = \frac{1}{2}n(a + L)$ for a.

5. Solve $L = a + (n - 1)d$ for n.

6. Solve $V = \frac{1}{3}\pi r^2 h$ for r.

7. Solve $A = 2\pi rh + \pi r^2$ for h.

8. Solve $\dfrac{F}{F_1} = \dfrac{2\pi L}{a}$ for L.

9. Solve $W = \dfrac{kbd^2}{L}$ for b.

10. Solve $S^2 = \dfrac{S^2}{4} + h^2$ for h.

11. Solve $\dfrac{a}{b} = \dfrac{c}{d}$ for a; for d.

12. Solve $A = \frac{1}{2}h(b_1 + b_2)$ for b_1. What is the value of b_1 when $A = 2400$, $h = 60$, and $b_2 = 50$?

13. Solve $I = Prt$ for r; for t. What is the value of r when $P = 1200$, $I = 210$, and $t = 3\frac{1}{2}$?

14. Solve $S = \dfrac{a + b + c}{2}$ for b. What is the value of b when $S = 30$, $a = 23.5$, and $c = 20.7$?

15. Solve $dr = DR$ for d.

16. Solve $ax - d = bx - c$ for x.

17. Solve $P = \dfrac{FH}{33,000}$ for F.

18. Solve $A = 2\pi(R - r)$ for r.

19. Solve $L = \pi(R + r) + 2d$ for d; for R.

20. Solve $V = \frac{1}{12}\pi h(2D^2 + d^2)$ for h.

21. Solve $\dfrac{P_2 - x}{x - P_1} = \dfrac{W_1}{W_2}$ for x.

22. Solve $I = \dfrac{En}{R + nr}$ for n.

23. Solve $A = td + b(s + n)$ for s.

24. The normal weight, W (in pounds), for a person of a certain height, h (in inches), is given approximately by the formula
$$W = 110 + \tfrac{11}{2}(h - 60).$$
Determine approximately the normal weight of a person of your height.

Applications of the Equation

Most of the problems that the student will meet in everyday life will be expressed in words and not in algebraic symbols. Before he can solve these problems, he must learn to translate English sentences into mathematical language. He will then find the equation a most important tool in solving problems. An example will illustrate this type of translation:

PROBLEM 1: How many pounds of cream testing 20% butterfat must be added to 80 lb of milk testing 3% butterfat to give milk testing 4.5% butterfat?

Analysis: Let x = number of pounds of cream to be added.

Then $0.20x$ = number of pounds of butterfat in this cream;

and $0.03(80)$ = number of pounds of butterfat in the 80 lb of milk.

$80 + x$ = number of pounds of final mixture,

and $0.045(80 + x)$ = number of pounds of butterfat in the final mixture.

Forming the equation: Now, is not the truth of the following statement evident?

"The number of pounds of butterfat in the unmixed quantities of milk and cream is the same as the number of pounds of butterfat in the final mixture."

This statement may be written:

"The number of pounds of butterfat in the 80 lb of milk plus the number of pounds of butterfat in the x lb of cream equals the number of pounds of butterfat in the final mixture."

Translated into the language of mathematics, this statement becomes the equation

$$0.03(80) + 0.20x = 0.045(80 + x).$$

When this equation is solved, our problem is solved. Solving, we obtain

$$2.40 + 0.20x = 3.600 + 0.045x.$$

$$0.20x - 0.045x = 3.6 - 2.4.$$

$$0.155x = 1.2.$$

$x = 7.7$, approximately, and we conclude that approximately 7.7 lb of cream are required in the mixture.

PROBLEM 2: A truck load of steers leaves a ranch at 5 A.M. and is followed $1\frac{1}{2}$ hours later by the rancher in his car. If the truck travels at 40 miles per hour and the car at 60, at what distance from the ranch should the car catch up with the truck?

In the analysis of this problem, two essential facts stand out. The first, relating to *time*, is stated in the problem: *The car's traveling time is $1\frac{1}{2}$ hours less than the truck's traveling time.* The second fact, relating to *distance*, becomes apparent to the *thinking student*: *the distances traveled by the car and the truck are equal.* Both of these facts must be involved in any procedure that leads to a solution of this problem, and *either* may serve as a basis for an equation.

First solution. To use the first of these facts as a basis for forming an equation, let x denote the number of miles traveled by the truck. Then it follows from the second fact mentioned above that x also denotes the number of miles traveled by the car. The traveling times of the truck and car can now be expressed in terms of x.

$$\frac{x}{40} = \text{the number of hours of traveling by the truck.}$$

$$\frac{x}{60} = \text{the number of hours of traveling by the car.}$$

The first of the above mentioned facts may now be restated as an equation:

$$\frac{x}{60} = \frac{x}{40} - 1\frac{1}{2}$$

Multiply both sides of the equation by 120 in order to clear the equation of fractions:

$$2x = 3x - 180.$$
$$-x = -180.$$
$$x = 180.$$

Conclusion: The car should overtake the truck at a point 180 miles from the ranch.

Second solution. Let t = the number of hours traveled by the truck. Then, according to the first above stated fact,

$$t - 1\frac{1}{2} = \text{number of hours traveled by the car.}$$

The distances involved can now be expressed in terms of t.

$$40t = \text{number of miles traveled by the truck.}$$
$$60(t - 1\frac{1}{2}) = \text{number of miles traveled by the car.}$$

Now, according to the second above mentioned fact, how must these two expressions of distance be related? Evidently

$$60(t - 1\frac{1}{2}) = 40t,$$

or
$$60t - 90 = 40t.$$

Whence
$$20t = 90,$$

and
$$t = 4\frac{1}{2}.$$

Conclusion: The truck travels for $4\frac{1}{2}$ hours, and at 40 miles per hour, goes a distance of 180 miles before being overtaken by the car.

In every practical problem in which the equation is used to obtain the solution, the student should be able to write out in words the statement of facts upon which his equation is based. In writing an equation one should always use abstract numbers rather than concrete numbers.

Problems

1. How many pounds of cream testing 25% butterfat must be added to 200 lb of 3.5% milk to make a 5% milk? By 3.5% milk is meant milk that tests 3.5% butterfat.

2. How many pounds each of 3.5% milk and 6.2% milk are required to make 100 lb of 4.5% milk?

3. How much skim milk must be mixed with 5.6% milk to make 100 lb of 4% milk? Consider the skim milk as containing no butterfat.

4. If 10 lb of 4.5% milk are mixed with 15 lb of 5.2% milk, the mixture should test what per cent butterfat?

5. How much water must be added to 24 oz of a 16% solution of salt to make a 2% solution?

6. How many gallons of water must be added to 20 gal of a winter spray of lime-sulfur testing 15% lime-sulfur, by volume, to make a summer spray which tests 5% lime-sulfur?

7. Counting 24 tablespoons to a pint, determine how many tablespoons of disinfectant should be added to a gallon of water to make a 10% solution.

8. A man has $12,000 invested at 3% per annum. How much additional should he have invested at 5% in order for his total annual income from the two investments to be $1000?

9. If a person has $9000 invested at 6%, how much may he invest at only 2.5% and still realize a return of 4% on his two investments?

10. Sound travels at about the rate of 1100 ft per second. How far from an observer is a gun whose flash is observed $1\frac{1}{2}$ sec before the report is heard?

11. Two automobiles start from points 225 miles apart toward each other on a straight road, one traveling at an average rate of 40 miles per hour and the other at 35 miles per hour. They should meet after how many hours?

12. The sum of the angles of a triangle is 180°. Find the angles of a triangle in which one angle is twice the size of the smallest angle and the largest angle is three times the size of the smallest angle.

13. It is estimated that a new set of spark plugs, costing $6.40, will increase the mileage of a certain car from 14 to 15 miles per gallon of gasoline. If gasoline costs 24¢ per gallon and the increased mileage is maintained sufficiently long, how many miles must the car be driven before the saving on gasoline pays for the new plugs?

14. A piece of wire 10 ft long is to be cut into two pieces so that the longer piece will be 6 in. more than twice as long as the shorter piece. Find the length of each piece.

15. A dealer pays $36 for a suit of clothes. At what price should he mark the suit so as to allow a discount of $33\frac{1}{3}\%$ of the marked price and still make a profit of 25% of the cost?

16. A dealer marked a pair of shoes at $12.95 but sold them at a discount of 20% and still made a profit of 25% of the cost. What did the shoes cost the dealer? If the shoes had been sold at the marked price, what would have been the per cent of profit?

17. How many pounds of cottonseed meal testing 41.9% crude protein should be added to 100 lb of feed testing 16.3% crude protein to produce a feed containing 23% crude protein?

18. How many pounds of acid phosphate should be added to 800 lb of cottonseed meal to form a fertilizer containing 10% phosphoric acid? Determine the per cent each of nitrogen and potash in the mixture.

19. How many pounds each of wood ashes and cottonseed meal should be used to form 1000 lb of fertilizer containing 3% potash?

20. A stock solution for an oil spray consists of 2 gal of oil weighing 7 lb 8 oz per gallon, 2 lb of soap, and 1 gal of water. Determine the per cent of oil in this stock solution.

21. How much water should be added to 1 gal of the stock solution mentioned in Problem 20 to make a winter spray testing 3% oil for use against the San Jose scale? (Disregard volume occupied by soap in solution.)

22. How much water should be added to 1 gal of the stock solution mentioned in Problem 20 to make a 1% oil spray for spraying citrus trees to control the red orange scale. (Disregard volume occupied by soap in solution.)

23. "Black Leaf 40" is a brand of nicotine sulfate which weighs about 10 lb to the gallon and tests 40% nicotine. If a spray used against plant lice consists of 1 pt of "Black Leaf 40" to 100 gal of water, what per cent "Black Leaf 40" does it contain? What per cent nicotine does it contain?

24. For use as a dip against sheep scab a solution testing 0.07% nicotine is formed by adding "Black Leaf 40" to water. How many pounds of "Black Leaf 40" should be added to 100 gal of water to make a dip of this strength? (See preceding problem.)

25. How many pounds of 20% acid phosphate should be used with a ton of 4-8-4 fertilizer to raise the phosphoric acid content to 12%?

26. If a 5-10-5 fertilizer has already been applied to a soil at the rate of

200 lb per acre, how many pounds of 16% acid phosphate should be used to result in a 24-lb per acre application of phosphoric acid?

27. Tests indicate that a certain soil needs to have 25 lb of nitrogen applied per acre to produce a good corn crop. If 300 lb of 5-10-5 fertilizer are applied per acre just prior to planting the corn, how many pounds of sodium nitrate testing 16% nitrogen should be applied as a side dressing to obtain the desired amount of nitrogen?

28. An application of 1 lb of commercial fertilizer per 100 sq ft of surface is equivalent to an application of how many pounds per acre?

29. How many pounds of ground ear corn testing 7.8% crude protein should be mixed with 100 lb of a 36% protein supplement to make a dairy feed whose crude protein content will be 18%?

30. With corn worth $1.80 per bushel and slaughter pigs worth 20¢ per pound of live weight, how many bushels of corn are equal in value to 100 lb of live-weight pork?

31. In estimating the number of acres, A, covered per hour by a farm machine moving at s miles per hour and having a cutting width of w ft, the formula

$$A = \frac{ws}{10}$$

is sometimes used. This formula makes appropriate allowance for the per cent of time usually lost in turning at ends, making adjustments, etc. Find the per cent of time lost implied by the formula.

32. Check the accuracy of the formula of Problem 31 by finding with it and by direct computation the capacity in acres per hour of an 8-ft tandem disk which is drawn at an average speed of 3 miles per hour, assuming that $17\frac{1}{2}\%$ of time is spent in operations that do not contribute to the acreage covered.

33. It is observed that a 2-row tractor cultivator averaging $2\frac{1}{4}$ miles per hour covers 18 acres in 10 hr in a field where the rows are 42 in. apart. Find the per cent of time that should be considered lost in nontillage operations.

34. An operator of a 1-row corn picker finds that he can harvest about 8 acres in a 10-hr day in a field in which the rows are 42 in. apart. If the machine moves along at an average speed of $2\frac{1}{4}$ miles an hour, find the per cent of time lost from the actual harvesting operation.

35. Most hay crops when first cut test from 75% to 82% moisture by weight. On a clear day with air at an average temperature of 78°F and 70% relative humidity, freshly cut alfalfa will dry in the field from a moisture content of 80% to one of 60% within four or five hours. How many pounds of alfalfa testing 80% moisture will dry to a ton of hay testing 60% moisture? How many pounds of water are evaporated in this drying process?

✓ **36.** How many pounds of air-dried alfalfa testing 60% moisture must be delivered to a mechanical drier to obtain a ton of hay testing 10% moisture? How many pounds of water are removed by the drier?

37. Per ton of hay of 10% moisture content delivered by a mechanical dryer, determine (a) the number of pounds of water removed from freshly cut hay testing 80% moisture (b) the number of pounds of the freshly cut hay required.

✓ **38.** The moisture content of alfalfa hay should be reduced to 20% or less for safe storage. How many tons of freshly cut alfalfa testing 75% moisture are required to yield 25 tons of storable hay?

✓ **39.** The maximum moisture content of grain sorghum for safe storage is 13%. A ton of freshly harvested grain sorghum testing 20% moisture, when run through a commercial drier, should yield how many pounds of grain testing 10% moisture?

✓ **40.** Suppose a trader is sure of a sale of 50 beef animals at 20¢ per pound of live weight, and he estimates that handling the cattle will incur a transportation cost to him of 60¢ per head and a shrinkage of 3% in weight. In order to make a profit of $5.00 per head how much per pound can he afford to pay for such animals averaging 800 lb in weight?

41. A certain dairy products firm buys whole milk at the following prices per 100 lb: $7.56 for milk testing 4% butterfat, $7.56 plus 7¢ for each 0.1% that the butterfat exceeds 4%, and $7.56 minus 7¢ for each 0.1% that the butterfat lacks of being 4%. Write a formula for the number of dollars, n, that would be paid for w pounds of milk testing r% butterfat.

42. Use the formula obtained in Problem 41 to find the sum that should be paid for 1200 lb of milk testing 4.8% butterfat.

43. Using the formula of Problem 41, find the sum that should be paid for 800 lb of milk testing 3.4% butterfat.

Systems of Linear Equations

Many problems require that the values of two or more unknown quantities be determined. In solving such problems it may be convenient to introduce several letters to represent the unknowns. It then becomes necessary to form as many equations as there are letters involved and to solve this group of equations. A group of equations under consideration at the same time is called a *system of simultaneous equations*.

Each equation of a system usually states a distinct relation that is true for many sets of values of the letters involved.

Consider the system:

$$\begin{cases} x + y = 5. \\ x - y = 1. \end{cases}$$

The first of these equations is satisfied by infinitely many pairs of corresponding values of x and y, a few of which appear in this table

Relation: $x + y = 5$							
x	-6	0	2	3	$3\frac{1}{4}$	5	8	370
y	11	5	3	2	$1\frac{3}{4}$	0	-3	-365

Each pair of satisfying values of x and y constitutes a *solution* of the equation. Likewise, the second equation has infinitely many solutions, some of which are here shown:

Relation: $x - y = 1$							
x	-3	0	1	2	3	$8\frac{1}{2}$	94	837
y	-4	-1	0	1	2	$7\frac{1}{2}$	93	836

By a *solution* of a *system of equations* is meant a set of values of the letters involved that satisfy all of the equations of the system. To *solve* a system of equations is to find *all* its solutions. In the above example it is evident that this system of equations is satisfied if $x = 3$ and $y = 2$, since this pair of values appears in both tables of solutions. This system of equations has only one solution, as is true of every system consisting of linear equations that are *independent* and *consistent*.

Equations are said to be independent if they express *distinct* relations between the variables* involved, and they are described as being consistent if the relations expressed are *not contradictory*.

Solving a system of two linear equations in two unknowns is usually brought about by combining, by addition or subtraction, the two members of one equation with the corresponding members of the other in such a way

---

* In this text, by a variable we shall mean a symbol, usually a letter, with which different values may be associated during its consideration.

as to eliminate one of the unknowns, thereby resulting in a third equation that contains only one unknown.

Example

Solve for x and y: $\begin{cases}(1) & 4x - 3y = 6. \\ (2) & x + 5y = 13.\end{cases}$

To eliminate x, multiply each side of Equation (2) by 4.   We then have

$$\begin{cases}(1) & 4x - 3y = 6. \\ (2) & 4x + 20y = 52.\end{cases}$$

Subtract: $-23y = -46.$

Divide by (-23): $y = 2.$

The value of x may be found by substituting 2 for y in either one of the original equations and solving the resulting equation in x.   Thus with $y = 2$, Equation (2) becomes

$$x + 5(2) = 13,$$

or $x + 10 = 13,$

from which $x = 3.$

The value of x might have been determined by multiplying each side of Equation (1) by 5 and each side of Equation (2) by 3 and adding, thereby eliminating y.

$$20x - 15y = 30.$$
$$3x + 15y = 39.$$
$$23x = 69.$$
$$x = 3.$$

The solution of the system of equations consists of the pair of numbers 3 and 2.   This means that each of the equations is a true statement if $x = 3$ and $y = 2$.

Method of substitution. Another way of eliminating one of the unknowns and thereby isolating the other unknown is to solve either of the equations for one unknown in terms of the other and substitute the expression obtained in the other equation.   In the example under consideration, fractions are avoided if Equation (2) is solved for x and the result is substituted in Equation (1), as demonstrated in the following:

$$\begin{array}{ll}(1) & \begin{cases}4x - 3y = 6. \\ x + 5y = 13.\end{cases} \\ (2) & \end{array}$$

Solve Equation (2) for x:

$$(2a) \quad x = 13 - 5y.$$

Substitute $(13 - 5y)$ for x in Equation (1):

$$4(13 - 5y) - 3y = 6.$$

Solve this equation for y:

$$52 - 20y - 3y = 6.$$
$$- 23y = -46.$$
$$y = 2.$$

Substitute 2 for y in Equation (2a):

$$x = 13 - 5(2).$$
$$= 13 - 10.$$
$$x = 3.$$

Conclusion: Both equations are satisfied if $x = 3$ and $y = 2$.

Problems

1. Solve for x and y:
$$\begin{cases} x + 2y = 7. \\ 5x - 2y = 11. \end{cases}$$

2. Solve for h and k:
$$\begin{cases} 10h - k = -3. \\ 12h + 12k = 102. \end{cases}$$

3. Solve for x and y:
$$\begin{cases} \dfrac{3x - 20}{2} = \dfrac{2x + 5y}{3}. \\ 10 = x - y. \end{cases}$$

4. Solve for m and n:
$$\begin{cases} 0.04m + 0.75n = 10. \\ 0.8m - 1.25n = 5. \end{cases}$$

5. Solve for x and y:
$$\begin{cases} x + y = 200. \\ 0.4x + 0.5y = 92. \end{cases}$$

6. How many pounds each of 3% milk and 5% milk should a farmer mix to make 100 lb of milk testing 4.5%?

7. An airplane flew 400 miles against the wind in 5 hr, and made the return trip in 3 hr 20 min. Assuming that the difference in time was due solely to the speed of the wind, find the speed of the airplane in still air and how fast the wind was blowing.

8. How many pounds of bone meal testing 3% nitrogen and 24% phosphoric acid and dried blood testing 13% nitrogen are needed for an acre of wheat ground which is strong in potash but which requires 12 lb of nitrogen and 20 lb of phosphoric acid per acre?

9. How many pounds of acid phosphate containing 16% phosphoric acid must be added to 800 lb of a 2-6-4 fertilizer to increase the per cent of phosphoric acid to 8%?

10. A feed dealer wishes to make up 1000 lb of corn chops, which he can sell at $3.60 per hundredweight, by mixing two grades, one retailing regularly at $3.00 and the other at $3.80 per hundredweight. How many pounds of each grade should he use?

11. How many pounds each of two kinds of grain, one worth $3.20 per hundredweight and the other worth $4.00 per hundredweight, should be used to form 1000 lb of a mixture worth $3.75 per hundredweight?

12. How many pounds each of two kinds of feed, one worth 3¢ a pound and one worth 5¢ a pound, are required to make 200 lb worth $3.75 per hundredweight?

13. How many pounds each of cottonseed meal and acid phosphate should be used to make 1000 lb of a fertilizer testing 4% nitrogen and 7.5% phosphoric acid? (The 1000 lb may include some filler.)

14. How many pounds each of acid phosphate, cottonseed meal, and muriate of potash should be used to make 1000 lb of a 4-7-4 fertilizer? (The 1000 lb may include some filler.)

15. A farmer has on hand one fertilizer labeled 3-8-4 and another labeled 5-10-5. How many pounds of each of these should he use per acre in order to supply the soil with 15 lb of nitrogen and 35 lb of phosphoric acid?

16. How many pounds each of bone meal and cottonseed meal should be applied to an acre of land to furnish the soil with 20 lb of nitrogen and 30 lb of phosphoric acid?

17. How many pounds each of Johnson grass hay testing 6% protein, and cottonseed cake testing 43% protein does it take to constitute 100 lb of feed, 12% of which is protein?

18. Find the number of pounds each of cottonseed meal testing 43% protein and cottonseed hulls testing 4.1% protein needed to make up a ton of feed that should test 16% protein.

19. How many pounds each of a grain mixture testing 10% digestible protein and silage testing 1.2% digestible protein are needed to supply a growing dairy animal with 25 lb of feed containing 1 lb of digestible protein?

20. How many pounds each of grain testing 7% digestible protein and tankage testing 34% digestible protein should be fed a 200-lb hog to give him a daily ration of 6 lb containing 1 lb of digestible protein?

21. From 100 bolls of cotton picked at random in a field, 485 locks of cotton are obtained. Knowing that some of the bolls contained 5 locks and the rest 4 locks each, how many of each kind of bolls were there? What per cent of the bolls may be considered 5-lock bolls?

22. In an offer of $3120 for 25 head of cattle, a prospective buyer claims to have evaluated some of the animals at $120 a head and the rest at $135. How many animals were rated at each of the values quoted?

23. For 40 dozen eggs a poultryman received $19.16 and was told that most of the eggs were being bought at 50¢ per dozen, while a few had to be classified as "small eggs" worth 43¢ a dozen. How many dozen were sold at each of these prices? What per cent of the eggs were classified as small?

24. From 100 sample stalks of corn, some bearing two ears and the rest one ear each, 172 ears of corn are picked. What per cent of the corn plants in the field may be considered as two-ear plants? (After using a system of equations in solving this problem, try to devise a simpler method of solving it.)

CHAPTER 4

LENGTHS, AREAS, AND VOLUMES

Measurements as Approximations

In actual practice, measurements of length, weight, volume, time, and so forth, are, in general, only approximations. For example, if we say that a certain piece of rope is 30 ft long, we really mean that it is approximately 30 ft long. It may be 29 ft 10 in. long; or perhaps 29 ft 10½ in. expresses more nearly the length of the rope. The fact is that it is usually impossible to state with certainty the exact length of the piece of rope. Such factors as inaccuracy of the measuring instruments, inability of a person to manipulate and read the instruments accurately, and the variable condition of the rope—its temperature, moisture content, degree of tension, and so forth—all tend to make the measurement inexact.

However, in most cases sufficient accuracy of measurement can be had for all ordinary purposes. It may be that strict adherence to 30 ft as the length of the piece of rope implies a greater degree of accuracy than is needed; that depends upon how the rope and the measure of its length are to be used.

In computations involving numbers which represent practical measurements the results should not indicate a higher degree of accuracy than is warranted by the precision of the measurements made. Particularly in performing a division in which the dividend is an approximation, the student should not continue a quotient to more and more decimal places by annexing zeros to the dividend.

Units of Measure

Measuring a quantity of any kind consists in comparing that quantity with a certain other quantity of the same kind, known as the *unit of measure*. For instance, to say that a board is 10 ft long means that its length is 10 times as great as a certain other length, called a *foot*, which is taken as a unit for measuring length. In a similar manner, to say that an

46

object weighs $86\frac{1}{2}$ lb means that the weight of the object is $86\frac{1}{2}$ times as great as a certain other weight, called a *pound*, which is taken as a unit for measuring weight.

The student is probably familiar with most of the units of measure in common use. However, certain units of measure may require a brief discussion.

Angles

If two straight line segments, OA and OB, proceed from the same point, they are said to form an angle. (See Fig. 1.) The point O is called the vertex of the angle, and the line segments OA and OB are called the *sides* of the angle. The angle may be denoted by the single letter O or by the symbol $\angle AOB$ (read "angle AOB").

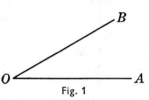

Fig. 1

The size of an angle does not depend upon the lengths of its sides. In fact, it is convenient to consider that the size of an angle is determined by the amount of turning that one line segment, say OA, must do about the point O in order to become coincident with the other line segment. If the line segment OA is rotated completely about the point O (so that it comes back to its original position), then OA is said to generate an angle of *one revolution*. The *revolution*, then, is a unit of angular measure. The unit of angular measure most often used is the *degree*, which may be defined as $\frac{1}{360}$ of a revolution. The degree is divided into 60 smaller units, called *minutes*, and the minute is further divided into 60 units called *seconds*. These relationships are shown in the following table:

> 1 revolution = 360 degrees, written 360°.
> 1 degree = 60 minutes, written 60'.
> 1 minute = 60 seconds, written 60".

An angle of 90° is called a *right angle*.

An angle of 180° is called a *straight angle*.

Angles less than 90° are said to be *acute*.

Angles greater than 90° and less than 180° are said to be *obtuse*.

If two intersecting line segments form a right angle, each line segment is said to be *perpendicular* to the other.

Areas

The term *area* signifies a *measure of surface*. While any specified portion of surface, regardless of shape, may be taken as a unit of area, the more commonly used units of area are squares whose sides are of such standard unit lengths as the inch, the centimeter, the foot, etc. Thus a square whose side is one inch long encloses a surface whose area is defined as being *one square inch* in size. Similarly, a one-foot square is said to have an area of *one square foot*, a one-mile square an area of *one square mile*, and so on.

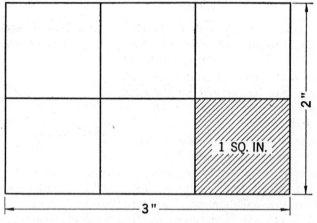

Fig. 2

The number of square inches, square feet, or square units of any kind contained within a figure is spoken of as the *area* of the figure. Note that if a rectangle 3 in. long and 2 in. wide is divided into 1-in. squares, as shown in Fig. 2, it is seen to have an area of 6 sq in. This area may be expressed in square feet by noting that

$$1 \text{ sq ft} = 144 \text{ sq in.,}$$
$$1 \text{ sq in.} = \tfrac{1}{144} \text{ sq ft,}$$

and

$$6 \text{ sq. in.} = 6(\tfrac{1}{144}) \text{ sq ft}$$
$$= \tfrac{6}{144} \text{ sq ft}$$
$$= \tfrac{1}{24} \text{ sq ft.}$$

It may be well to point out that it is not necessary that a surface be rectangular in shape in order to have area. Thus, triangles, circles, spheres, and various other figures have area even though they cannot be pictured as consisting of whole square blocks representing the particular unit of area employed.

Volumes

The term *volume* applies to a *measure of space*. While any specified portion of space, regardless of shape, may be chosen as a unit of volume, the more commonly used units of volume are cubes whose edges have

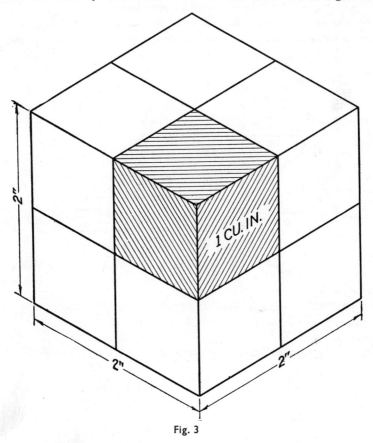

Fig. 3

standard unit lengths. Thus, a cube whose edge is one inch long is considered as containing or occupying a space whose volume is *one cubic inch*, and a one-foot cube has a volume of *one cubic foot*. The number of cubic units of any kind contained in a figure is spoken of as the *volume* of the figure. If a box-shaped figure 2 in. long, 2 in. wide, and 2 in. high is divided into 1-in. cubes, as illustrated in Fig. 3, it is seen to have a volume of 8 cu in. Note that a 2-in. cube is really eight times as large as a 1-in. cube.

Of course, it is not necessary that a body be boxlike in shape in order to have volume. Anything that occupies space (or takes up room) has volume, and such volume is expressible in terms of any specified unit even though the space being measured may not be pictured as consisting of whole cube-shaped blocks representing that unit.

On the next few pages an outline of the plane and solid figures most often involved in practical measurements is given. The student should find the formulas useful in computing distances, areas, and volumes.

Plane Figures

1. Triangle (figure bounded by three straight line segments).

    (a) General Triangle (triangle of any shape).

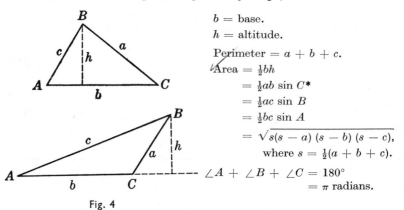

b = base.

h = altitude.

Perimeter $= a + b + c$.

Area $= \frac{1}{2}bh$

$= \frac{1}{2}ab \sin C$*

$= \frac{1}{2}ac \sin B$

$= \frac{1}{2}bc \sin A$

$= \sqrt{s(s - a)(s - b)(s - c)}$,

    where $s = \frac{1}{2}(a + b + c)$.

$\angle A + \angle B + \angle C = 180°$

$= \pi$ radians.

Fig. 4

    (b) Isosceles Triangle (triangle which has two sides equal).

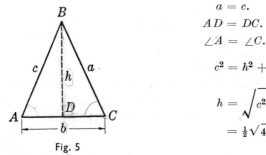

$a = c$.

$AD = DC$.

$\angle A = \angle C$.

$c^2 = h^2 + \left(\dfrac{b}{2}\right)^2$.

$h = \sqrt{c^2 - \dfrac{b^2}{4}}$

$= \frac{1}{2}\sqrt{4c^2 - b^2}$.

Fig. 5

---

* Sin A, sin B, and sin C are trigonometric functions, which will be explained in Chapter 6.

(c) Equilateral Triangle (triangle whose sides are equal).

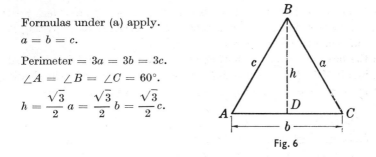

Formulas under (a) apply.

$a = b = c.$

Perimeter $= 3a = 3b = 3c.$

$\angle A = \angle B = \angle C = 60°.$

$h = \dfrac{\sqrt{3}}{2}\, a = \dfrac{\sqrt{3}}{2}\, b = \dfrac{\sqrt{3}}{2}\, c.$

Fig. 6

(d) Right Triangle (triangle in which one angle is 90°).

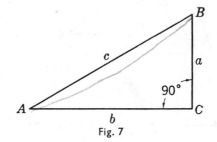

Formulas under (a) apply.

Area $= \frac{1}{2}ba.$

$c^2 = a^2 + b^2.$

(A more complete discussion of the right triangle is given in chapter 61.)

Fig. 7

2. Quadrilateral (plane figure bounded by four straight lines).

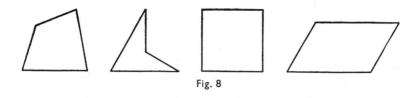

Fig. 8

Perimeter = sum of sides.

Area: There is no simple general formula for the area. In the following sections formulas are given for the areas of certain types of quadrilaterals.

(a) Trapezium (quadrilateral in which no two sides are parallel).

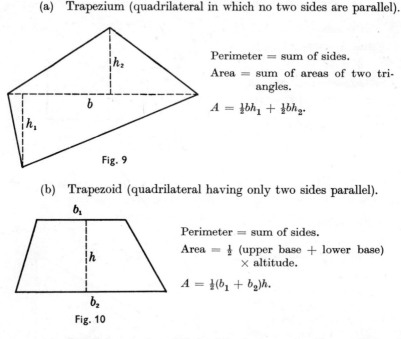

Perimeter = sum of sides.

Area = sum of areas of two triangles.

$A = \frac{1}{2}bh_1 + \frac{1}{2}bh_2.$

Fig. 9

(b) Trapezoid (quadrilateral having only two sides parallel).

Perimeter = sum of sides.

Area = $\frac{1}{2}$ (upper base + lower base)
× altitude.

$A = \frac{1}{2}(b_1 + b_2)h.$

Fig. 10

(c) Parallelogram (quadrilateral having opposite sides parallel and
equal).

Perimeter = (2 × longer side) + (2
× shorter side).

Area = base × altitude.

$A = bh.$

Fig. 11

(d) Rectangle (parallelogram whose angles are right angles).

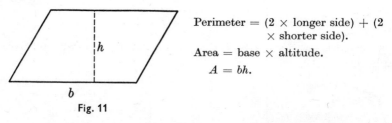

Perimeter = (2 × base) + (2 × altitude).

Area = base × altitude.

$A = bh.$

Diagonal = $\sqrt{(\text{base})^2 + (\text{altitude})^2}$

$d = \sqrt{b^2 + h^2}.$

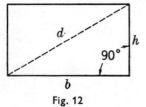

Fig. 12

(e) Square (rectangle whose sides are equal).

Perimeter = 4 × side.
Area = (side)^2.
$A = s^2$.
Diagonal = $\sqrt{2}$ × side.
$\quad\quad d = \sqrt{2}s$
or $\quad\quad d = s\sqrt{2}$.

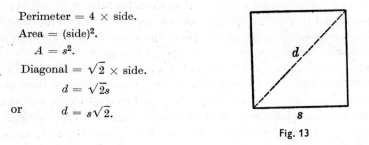

Fig. 13

3. Circle (plane figure bounded by a curved line, all points of which are equidistant from a fixed point called the center).

O = center.
π = 3.1416, approximately
$\quad$ = $\frac{22}{7}$, approximately.
r = radius.
d = diameter.
c = circumference.
A = area.

$d = 2r$.
$c = 2\pi r = \pi d$.
$A = \pi r^2$.

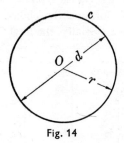

Fig. 14

4. Sector of a Circle (portion of circle bounded by two radii and their intercepted arc).

r = radius.
S = arc.
D = degrees in central angle.
A = area.

$S = \dfrac{\pi r D}{180°}$.

$A = \frac{1}{2} rS$
$\quad = \dfrac{\pi r^2 D}{360°}$.

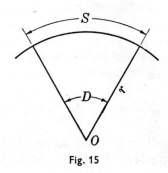

Fig. 15

5.   The Trapezoidal Rule for Approximate Area.   If a figure is bounded on one side by an irregular curve and on the other sides by straight lines, as illustrated in Fig. 16, the approximate area of the figure can usually be expressed satisfactorily as the sum of the areas of a number of trapezoids constructed as follows. The base line, AB, is divided into n segments of equal length d, and at each point of division of AB, as well as at A and B, perpendiculars are erected. The points of intersection of these perpendiculars with the curve CD are then joined by straight line segments, so that n trapezoids are formed. If the lengths of the $(n+1)$ perpendicular segments extending from AB to points on CD are denoted by $h_0, h_1, h_2, \ldots,$ h_n, the approximate area of the figure $ABCD$ is given by the formula

$$\text{Area} = d(\tfrac{1}{2}h_0 + h_1 + h_2 + \ldots + h_{n-1} + \tfrac{1}{2}h_n).$$

For any particular choice of n, the student may readily verify that this formula gives the sum of the areas of the n trapezoids. In an application of the formula the choice of n depends upon the degree of accuracy desired—usually, the larger n is, the better is the approximation.

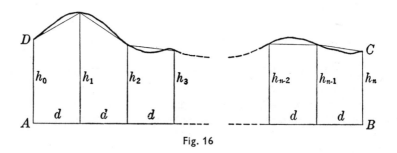

Fig. 16

6.   Simpson's Rule.   Another method of approximating the area of a figure of the type illustrated by Fig. 16 is based upon the assumption that the figure is divided into an *even* number of vertical strips of equal width and bounded above by arcs of parabolas. This method leads to Simpson's rule for approximate area:

$$\text{Area} = \frac{d}{3}\,(h_0 + 4h_1 + 2h_2 + 4h_3 + 2h_4 + \ldots + 4h_{n-1} + h_n).$$

Note that with an *even* number of strips as required there is an *odd* number of height measurements $h_0, h_1, h_2, \ldots, h_n$.

Solids

1. Rectangular Solid (solid bounded by six rectangles).

Volume = length × width
          × depth.

$V = l \times w \times h.$

Area of surface = sum of the
                  areas of the
                  six rectan-
                  gular faces.

$A = 2lw + 2lh + 2wh.$

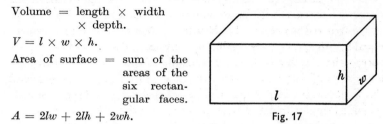

Fig. 17

2. Cube (rectangular solid whose edges are all equal).

Volume = (edge)^3.

$V = x^3.$

Area of surface = 6 × (edge)^2.

$A = 6x^2.$

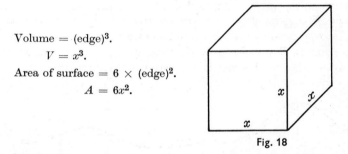

Fig. 18

3. Right Prism (solid bounded by two* polygons, called the bases, which are congruent† and lie in parallel planes, and a number of rectangular lateral faces perpendicular to the bases, there being a lateral face passing through each pair of corresponding sides of the two polygons).

h = altitude.

A = area of base.

Lateral area = sum of areas of
               lateral faces.

Total area = lateral area + area
             of bases.

Volume = Ah.

(Note that this formula for volume applies to right cylinders also and that a rectangular solid is a special type of prism.)

Fig. 19

---

* A *polygon* is a plane closed figure bounded by straight lines.

† Two polygons are said to be *congruent* if they have the same size and shape.

4. Right Circular Cylinder (solid generated by revolving a rectangle about one of its sides).

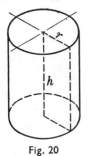

Fig. 20

r = radius.
h = altitude.
Volume = $\pi r^2 h$.
Lateral area = $2\pi r h$.
Total surface area = $2\pi r h + 2\pi r^2$.

5. Right Circular Cone (solid generated by revolving a right triangle about one of its legs).

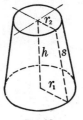

Fig. 21

r = radius of base.
h = altitude.
s = slant height.
Volume = $\frac{1}{3}\pi r^2 h$.
Lateral area = $\pi r s$.
Total area = $\pi r s + \pi r^2$.

6. Frustum of Right Circular Cone (portion of a right circular cone included between the base and a cross section parallel to the base).

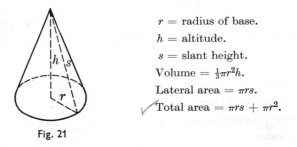

Fig. 22

h = altitude.
A_1 = area of lower base of radius r_1.
A_2 = area of upper base of radius r_2.
s = slant height.
C_1 = circumference of lower base.
C_2 = circumference of upper base.

$$\text{Volume} = \frac{h}{3}\left(A_1 + A_2 + \sqrt{A_1 A_2}\right)$$

$$= \frac{\pi h}{3}\left(r_1^2 + r_1 r_2 + r_2^2\right).$$

$$\text{Lateral area} = s\,\frac{(C_1 + C_2)}{2}.$$

7. **Regular Pyramid** (solid bounded by three or more congruent triangles having a common vertex and a regular polygon whose sides are the bases of the triangles).

A = area of base.

h = altitude.

s = slant height.

P = perimeter of base.

Volume = $\frac{1}{3}Ah$.

Lateral area = $\dfrac{Ps}{2}$.

Fig. 23

8. **Frustum of Regular Pyramid** (portion of a regular pyramid included between the base and a cross section parallel to the base).

h = altitude.

A_1 = area of lower base.

A_2 = area of upper base.

V = volume.

$$V = \frac{h}{3}(A_1 + A_2 + \sqrt{A_1 A_2}).$$

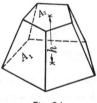

Fig. 24

9. **Sphere** (solid bounded by a curved surface all points of which are equidistant from a fixed point called the center).

r = radius.

Volume = $\frac{4}{3}\pi r^3$.

Area = $4\pi r^2$.

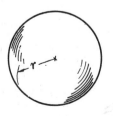

Fig. 25

10.   Barrel.

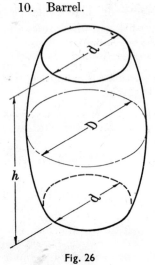

Fig. 26

D = middle diameter.

d = end diameter.

h = height.

Volume = $\frac{1}{12}\pi h(2D^2 + d^2)$, approximately.

The formula just given is a special application of a more general formula

$$V = \frac{h}{6}(B_1 + B_2 + 4A)$$

in which B_1 and B_2 are the areas of the parallel bases of a solid, A is the area of the middle cross section, and h is the altitude. This formula may properly be called a *master formula*, since, except for the barrel, it gives the *exact volume* of every solid considered thus far, applying even where one or both of the bases reduce to a point as in the cases of the cone and the sphere.

11. Torus, or Anchor Ring (solid obtained by revolving a circle about an axis in the plane of the circle and not intersecting the circle).

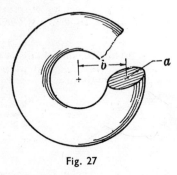

Fig. 27

a = radius of circle.

b = distance from center of circle to axis of revolution.

Surface area = $4\pi^2 ab$.

Volume = $2\pi^2 a^2 b$.

Problems

1. How many square yards of canvas are required for the walls and ceiling of a room 16 by 18 ft if the walls are 9 ft high and a deduction of one-fifth the area of the walls is made on account of windows and doors?

P. 5° for Oct 9

2. How many acres are there in a rectangular field 1580 ft long and 675 ft wide?

3. How many square feet of sheet iron are required to make the bottom and wall of a cylindrical cistern 6 ft in diameter and 8 ft high?

4. What must be the length of a binding rod for a cylindrical silo 14 ft in diameter if 1 ft is allowed for overlapping?

5. Find the number of acres in a field that is practically in the form of a trapezoid whose bases are 140 yd and 105 yd and whose altitude is 70 yd.

6. If a room is heated by 210 ft of steam pipe 2 in. in diameter, what is the area of the radiating surface?

7. What is the diameter of a tree around which a 16-ft rope will just reach?

8. How many squares of roofing are required for a gable roof each side of which is a rectangle about 18 ft by 53 ft? How much will the roofing cost at $7.20 per square if it cannot be bought in lots of less than ½ square?

9. About how many gallons of paint should be required for two coats on the walls of a barn 32 by 48 ft if the walls are 12 ft high and no allowance is made for openings?

10. A silo is 16 ft in diameter and 36 ft high. About how many gallons of paint would be required to give the wall of the silo two coats?

11. Each of two portions of a hip roof is a trapezoid with bases of 40 and 25 ft and an altitude of 18 ft, and each of two portions is an isosceles triangle with a base of 20 ft and an altitude of 20 ft. How many 4-in. shingles should be required for the roof?

12. How many revolutions per second is a 30-in. (outside diameter) automobile wheel making when the automobile is travelling 40 miles per hour?

13. A 3-ft walk is constructed around a circular pool whose diameter is 80 ft. At $3.20 per square yard what is the cost of the walk?

14. Find the total pressure on a piston 6 in. in diameter when the pressure gauge registers 140 lb per square inch.

15. How many square yards of canvas are there in a conical tent whose base is 14 ft in diameter and whose slant height is 12 ft?

16. Allowing 2 in. for rolling at the edges, how many square feet of tin are required in making 120 ft of gutter whose cross section is a semi-circle 3½ in. in diameter? (Use $\frac{22}{7}$ for π.)

17. Counting three pickets 2 in. by 1 in. by 4 ft for each linear foot of fence, determine how many gallons of paint are required to give 100 ft of picket fence two coats.

18-22. Find the number of acres in the fields represented by Figs. 28–32. The figures are not to be considered as drawn to scale.

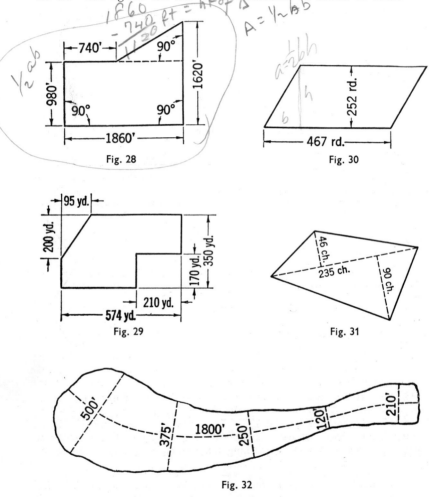

Fig. 28

Fig. 30

Fig. 29

Fig. 31

Fig. 32

23-27. Assume that Figs. 33–37 are each drawn to scale in representing a certain field. By measuring the side of the drawing upon which is written the length of the corresponding side of the field, determine the scale used. Then find approximately the lengths of other field lines needed in computing the area, dotting in auxiliary lines. Finally, compute the approximate area of the field.

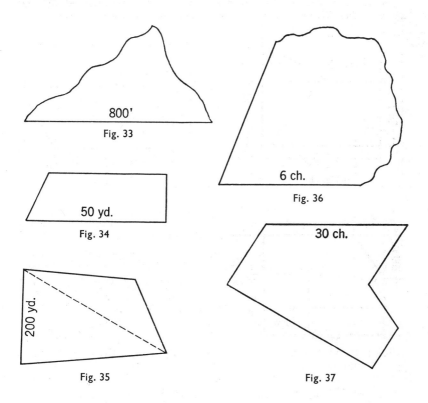

Fig. 33

50 yd.

Fig. 34

6 ch.

Fig. 36

200 yd.

Fig. 35

30 ch.

Fig. 37

28. In Fig. 16, page 54, fill in the breaks in the curved line CD and the base line AB and insert another altitude, h_4, halfway between the one labeled h_3 and the one labeled h_{n-2}. Then consider the figure $ABCD$ as having been drawn to scale in representing a certain field whose side corresponding to AB is 100 chains long, and find approximately the number of acres in the field.

29. Fig. 38 is a drawing made from a portion of an aerial photographic map used in measuring acreages in connection with the Government's farm program. The portion here shown pictures all of a certain farm. The scale is 1 in. to 660 ft. In practice, areas are usually obtained from such pictures by use of a planimeter. However, fairly satisfactory approximations may be computed from carefully made measurements of lengths on the field pictures.   Determine approximately the number of acres in each of the fields lettered.

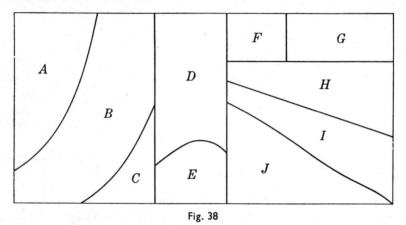

Fig. 38

30.   A wheat bin is 8 ft long, 6 ft wide, and 4 ft deep.   How many bushels of wheat does it contain if it is three-fourths full?

31.   About how many cubic yards of earth are removed in making a pond which is almost in the form of a hemisphere, the greatest depth being 9 ft?   How many gallons of water should the pond hold when it is full?

32.   About how many tons of silage are there in a cylindrical silo whose inside diameter is 12 ft and whose height is 30 ft if the silage lacks 5 ft of reaching the top?

33.   How many gallons of water does a cylindrical tank 5 ft in diameter and 7 ft high hold when it is full?   How much does this volume of water weigh?

34.   At 62½¢ per cubic yard what is the cost of excavation for a cellar 24 by 18 by 9 ft?

35.   About how many tons of hay are there in a stack 10 ft high, 30 ft long, 16 ft wide at the base, and 8 ft wide at the top?   (Volume = area of cross section × length.)

36.   The interior of a freight car is 8 ft wide, 34 ft long, and 7 ft high. If it is filled with wheat to a depth of 5 ft, what is the approximate weight of the wheat?

37.   How many cords of wood are there in a stack 8 ft wide, 8 ft high, and 40 ft long?

38.   About how many bricks are needed in building a wall 42 ft long, 1½ ft thick, and 6¼ ft high?   At $9 per thousand what should be the cost of the bricks?

39. About how many bricks are required for the wall of an underground cylindrical cistern 7 ft in inside diameter and 15 ft deep if the wall is 4 in. thick? (Assume that the difference in outside and inside circumference is taken care of by wedgelike vertical mortar joints.)

40. If a haystack is considered as a right circular cylinder 10 ft in diameter and 15 ft high, how many tons of hay does it contain?

41. An ordinary farm-wagon box is 10 ft long, 3 ft wide, and 2 ft deep. About how many bushels of shelled corn will it hold? About how many bushels of dry sound corn in the ear will it hold?

42. Find the capacity in gallons of a vessel 20 in. deep whose bottom and top diameters are 7 in. and 14 in., respectively. (Apply the formula for the volume of the frustum of a cone.)

43. How many cubic feet of concrete are there in the wall of a cylindrical silo whose inside diameter is 12 ft and whose wall is 8 in. thick and 30 ft high?

44. A hog trough of triangular cross section measures 16 in. across the top, $8\frac{1}{2}$ in. in depth, and 4 ft in length (inside measurement). How many gallons of water will it hold? (In this case, note that volume = area of cross section × length.)

45. A compartment with a capacity of 1 cu yd is to be formed in an ordinary farm-wagon box by a partition placed across the wagon. How long should the compartment be? (See Problem 41.)

46. How high must a bin be made to hold 360 bu of wheat if it is to be built on floor space 10 ft long and 5 ft wide?

47. What should be the length of a field 30 chains wide if the field is to contain 150 acres?

48. At what height above the bottom of an ordinary wagon box should a mark be made to have the wagon contain a cubic yard when filled to that mark? (See Problem 41.)

49. In order to determine approximately the number of cubic feet per bushel to be allowed in measuring a certain lot of ear corn, a man shells a representative sample of 1 cu ft of the ear corn and finds that the shelled corn weighs 22 lb. This result indicates how many cubic feet to the bushel?

50. How many bushels of ear corn of the kind mentioned in the preceding problem should there be in a truckload if the truck bed is 12 ft long, 5 ft wide, and 4 ft deep?

51. Water is being pumped into a cylindrical tank 14 ft in diameter at a rate such that, if no water is being drawn off, the water level rises 1 ft in 20 min. How many gallons of water per hour are being delivered by the pump?

52. The cross section of a certain stream is practically a rectangle 20 ft long and 8 ft deep. It is observed that a piece of cork floats downstream a distance of 200 ft in 3 min. If the mean velocity of the water is taken as 0.8 of the surface velocity, about how many gallons of water per hour pass a given point in the stream?

53. If a certain pipe 2 in. in diameter discharges 6 gal of water per minute, determine the velocity of the water in feet per second at the point of issuance from the pipe.

54. How many gallons of water per minute will be discharged by a pipe 1½ in. in diameter if the water has a velocity of 1¼ ft per second?

55. How many feet deep should ear corn be piled in a crib 15 ft long, 12 ft wide, and 10 ft deep to have the crib contain 250 bu of corn?

56. Determine the dimensions of a rectangular piece of tin that can be bent to form the wall of a cylindrical can 4 in. in diameter and 4½ in. tall, allowing ¼ in. for overlapping at the joint.

57. How many square feet of sheet iron are required for the wall of a cylindrical tank 7 ft in diameter and 8 ft high if a 9-in. strip 8 ft long is allowed for overlapping?

58. How many feet deep should wheat be placed in a crib 12 ft long, 10 ft wide, and 8 ft high so that the crib will contain 480 bu of wheat?

59. How many feet deep should water be in a cylindrical tank 7 ft in diameter and 7 ft tall to have the tank contain 1000 gal of water?

60. Find in feet per minute the speed of a belt being driven by a pulley 7 in. in diameter and making 1650 rpm (revolutions per minute), assuming that belt slippage is negligible.

61. A square inch is equivalent to how many square centimeters?

62. A cubic inch is equivalent to how many cubic centimeters?

63. An ounce (avoirdupois) is equivalent to how many grams?

64. A pound is equivalent to how many grams? A pound is equivalent to how many kilograms?

65. A liter is equivalent to how many cubic inches?

66. The specific gravity of a substance is defined as the ratio of the weight of any volume of the substance to the weight of an equal volume of water. Since 1 cc of water at 4°C weighs 1 g, the specific gravity of a substance may be considered as the number of grams in the weight of 1 cc of the substance. If alcohol has a specific gravity of 0.82, how much do 150 cc of alcohol weigh?

67. If a 10% solution of menthol in alcohol has a specific gravity of 0.854, what volume (in cubic centimeters) should 128 g of the solution have?

68. Glycerin has a specific gravity of 1.25. How much do 150 cc of glycerin weigh? How many cubic centimeters of glycerin weigh 75 g?

69. How many grams of silver nitrate should be dissolved in water to form 150 g of solution testing 10% silver nitrate?

70. How many grams of sodium chloride should be dissolved in water to form 1500 g of a 16% solution of the salt?

71. How many grams of sodium chloride should be added to 1500 cc of water to form a 16% solution of the salt?

72. How many grams each of menthol and alcohol are required to make 150 g of a 10% solution of menthol in alcohol? If the alcohol has a specific gravity of 0.82, how many cubic centimeters are required?

73. In how much water should $\frac{1}{2}$ lb of salt be dissolved to form a 15% solution of salt?

74. How many grams of 5% soda solution can be made from 250 g of soda?

75. If 65 grains of salt are dissolved in 400 grains of water, what per cent of the resulting solution is salt?

76. If 300 cc of water are combined with 500 cc of nitric acid having a specific gravity of 1.4, what per cent (by weight) of the resulting product is nitric acid?

77. Suppose that a pharmacist is directed to provide exactly 100 cc of a 15% (by weight) solution of a certain salt in water and that the specific gravity of the desired solution is not known. How can he fill the prescription? (*Suggestion:* The pharmacist may use 100 cc of water, which weighs 100 g, to make more than 100 cc of the 15% solution and then use only 100 cc of the solution in filling the prescription.)

78. A physician orders 240 cc of a 3% (by weight) solution of mercuric chloride in water. How can the order be filled?

79. A speed of 40 miles per hour is equivalent to a speed of how many feet per second?

80. A wheel 27 in. in diameter on a car traveling 40 miles per hour is making how many revolutions per minute?

81. How many acres are there in a tract of land which appears on a map as an 8 by 12-in. rectangle if the scale of the map is 1 in. to 660 ft?

82. What scale in yards to the inch is employed on a map if a tract of land known to contain 240 acres appears as a rectangle 3.3 in. long and 2.2 in. wide?

83. A hay barn 48 ft long, 36 ft wide, and 12 ft tall will hold about how many bales of hay, the bales averaging 36 in. in length and 14 by 18 in. in rectangular cross section?

84. Find the pressure, in pounds per square inch, acting on the bottom of a cylindrical tank 7 ft in diameter and 8 ft tall, when the tank is full of water.

85. The total force acting outwardly against the inner surface of the vertical wall of a tank filled with water is equivalent to the force that would act upon a plane horizontal surface of equal area submerged at a depth equal to half the height of water in the tank. Find the total force acting on the vertical wall of the tank described in the preceding problem.

86. Find the number of miles traveled in plowing an acre of land if all the soil is turned by making singly successive furrows 6 in. wide. (In this and similar problems disregard the distance traveled in making turns at ends of furrows.)

87. With a plow that cuts a 10-in. slice of soil, how many miles does a person travel in completely breaking a 10-acre field?

88. How many miles should a 12-in. plow travel in completely breaking an acre of soil?

89. A tractor pulling a gang of two 12-in. plows travels how many miles in "flat breaking" a 40-acre field?

90. A tractor equipped with a 7-ft cycle can mow at most how many acres per 10-hr day if its average rate of travel is 4 miles per hour?

91. A 2-row corn planter is pulled by a tractor at average speed of 3 miles per hour. About how many acres does it plant in a 10-hr day if the rows are 42 in. apart and if about 20% of the time is spent in making turns, refilling seed box, and making necessary adjustments?

92. A 2-row corn picker traveling at an average speed of $2\frac{1}{2}$ miles per hour should harvest about how many acres of corn in a 10-hr day if the rows are 42 in. apart and if 25% of the time is spent in making turns, exchanging full trailer for empty trailer, etc.?

93. The owner of a tractor-type corn picker charges $3.00 per acre for custom harvesting. If the machine harvests an average of 12 acres per 10-hr day, find the cost per hour for this service and find the cost of harvesting per bushel of corn if the yield is 60 bu per acre.

94. A 2-horse team pulls a 5-ft mower at a speed of $2\frac{1}{4}$ miles per hour. If it is estimated that one-sixth of the time is lost in turning at ends, making adjustments, etc., find approximately the number of hours required to cut a 20-acre field of sorghum.

95. A tractor traveling at the rate of $2\frac{1}{2}$ miles per hour and pulling two 12-in. plows will plow how many acres in an hour, making no allowance for time lost in turning, etc.?

96. A 2-row cotton picker travels at a speed of 2 miles per hour along rows 40 in. apart in a field whose yield averages $\frac{3}{4}$ bale per acre. Assuming that about one-seventh of the time spent in the field is required for end-of-row turning, unloading machine, and making necessary adjustments, how many bales of cotton should the machine harvest in a 10-hr day?

97. A sample bale of hay from a block-shaped stack measures 16 by 20 by 42 in. and weighs 65 lb. About how many tons of hay are there in the stack if it is 80 ft long, 30 ft wide, and 20 ft tall?

98. About how many tons of hay like that of the preceding problem will a box car hold if it measures 50 by 9 by 11 ft?

99. A truck with a capacity for hauling 150 bales will make about how many trips in delivering the hay (like that of Problem 97) from two full railroad cars each measuring 40 by 9 by 12 ft?

100. Assume that in the operation of field machines about $17\frac{1}{2}\%$ of the time is spent in end-of-row turning and other nonacreage gaining effort; then show that the number of acres covered per hour by a machine is given approximately by the formula

$$A = \frac{1}{10} ws$$

where A is the number of acres, w is the effective tillage or cutting width of machine in feet, and s is speed of machine in miles per hour.

CHAPTER 5

RATIO AND PROPORTION

Ratio

The ratio of one number to another is simply the common fraction obtained by dividing the one by the other. For example, the ratio of 3 to 5 is $\frac{3}{5}$ (sometimes written 3 : 5). The ratio of 8 in. to 12 in. is

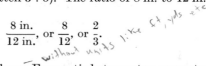

$$\frac{8 \text{ in.}}{12 \text{ in.}}, \text{ or } \frac{8}{12}, \text{ or } \frac{2}{3}.$$

Ratios are abstract numbers. For a ratio between two concrete numbers to have meaning, the concrete numbers must be of the same kind; that is, they must be expressed in terms of the same unit.

Proportion

A proportion is simply an equation between two ratios. Hence a proportion involving an unknown is solved by the methods used in solving a fractional equation.

Example

Find the value of x if 3 is to x as 6 is to 35.

This statement may be written

$$3 : x = 6 : 35.$$

The preferred form, however, is

$$\frac{3}{x} = \frac{6}{35}.$$

Multiply each side by $35x$:

$$105 = 6x.$$

Divide each side by 6:

$$x = \frac{105}{6} = \frac{35}{2} = 17\frac{1}{2}.$$

68

If four numbers $a, b, c,$ and d, none of which is zero, satisfy the proportion

$$(1) \quad \frac{a}{b} = \frac{c}{d},$$

it follows that they satisfy also the proportions

$$(2) \quad \frac{a}{c} = \frac{b}{d}$$

and

$$(3) \quad \frac{b}{a} = \frac{d}{c}.$$

The student should verify these statements.

Suppose that for each applicable value of a variable x another variable y has a corresponding value and that y_1 and y_2 are values of y that correspond, respectively, to the values x_1 and x_2 of x. Then to say that y *is proportional to* x means that y_1 is to y_2 as x_1 is to x_2; that is,

$$\frac{y_1}{y_2} = \frac{x_1}{x_2}.$$

If both sides of this equation are multiplied by y_2/x_1 the relation appears in the form

$$\frac{y_1}{x_1} = \frac{y_2}{x_2}.$$

This equation may now be interpreted as saying that the ratio of y to x, that is y/x, is the same or *constant* for all pairs of corresponding values of x and y. In other words, there must be some *constant number*, which we may denote by k, such that

$$\frac{y}{x} = k$$

or

$$y = kx.$$

In fact, the equation $y = kx$ is considered the way of expressing mathematically each of the following statements.

(1) y is proportional to x.

(2) y is directly proportional to x.

(3) y varies as x.

(4) y varies directly as x.

To say that y is *inversely proportional to* x means that y_1 is to y_2 as x_2 is to x_1; that is,

$$\frac{y_1}{y_2} = \frac{x_2}{x_1}.$$

If each side of this equation is multiplied by $x_1 y_2$ the relation appears in the form

$$x_1 y_1 = x_2 y_2.$$

This may be interpreted as saying that the product xy is constant for every pair of corresponding values of x and y. In this case, there must be a constant number k such that

$$xy = k$$

or

$$y = \frac{k}{x}.$$

The equation $y = k/x$ is considered the mathematical translation of each of these statements:

(1) y is inversely proportional to x.

(2) y varies inversely as x.

Finally, to say that y is proportional to x and t, and varies inversely as w, we write

$$y = \frac{kxt}{w}$$

where k is a constant. In all the above equations k is called the *constant of proportionality*.

Stated below are a few principles whose applications may involve proportions.

1. The distance traveled by a body moving at a constant rate is proportional to the time of traveling. If a man can walk d_1 mi. in t_1 hr and maintains this rate for t_2 hr, the number, d_2, of miles walked in t_2 hr is given by the proportion

$$\frac{d_2}{d_1} = \frac{t_2}{t_1}.$$

2. The cost of a number of articles bought at a fixed price per article is proportional to the number of articles bought. If N_1 acres of land are

bought for P_1 dollars, then the cost, P_2 dollars, of N_2 acres bought at the same price per acre is given by the proportion

$$\frac{P_2}{P_1} = \frac{N_2}{N_1}.$$

3. Two geometric figures are considered similar if lengths measured on one of them are proportional to corresponding lengths measured on the other.

4. The areas of two similar plane figures are proportional to the squares of corresponding length measurements.

5. The volumes of two similar solids are proportional to the cubes of corresponding length measurements.

The proportions accompanying Figs. 39–42 illustrate how principles 3, 4, and 5 apply. In the proportions stated, the V's represent volumes, the A's represent areas, and the other letters represent lengths.

Similar Triangles

(1) $\dfrac{l_1}{l_2} = \dfrac{b_1}{b_2} = \dfrac{h_1}{h_2}.$

(2) $\dfrac{A_1}{A_2} = \dfrac{b_1^{\,2}}{b_2^{\,2}} = \dfrac{h_1^{\,2}}{h_2^{\,2}} = \dfrac{l_1^{\,2}}{l_2^{\,2}}.$

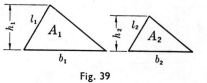

Fig. 39

Circles

(1) $\dfrac{C_1}{C_2} = \dfrac{r_1}{r_2} = \dfrac{d_1}{d_2}.$

(2) $\dfrac{A_1}{A_2} = \dfrac{r_1^{\,2}}{r_2^{\,2}} = \dfrac{C_1^{\,2}}{C_2^{\,2}} = \dfrac{d_1^{\,2}}{d_2^{\,2}}.$

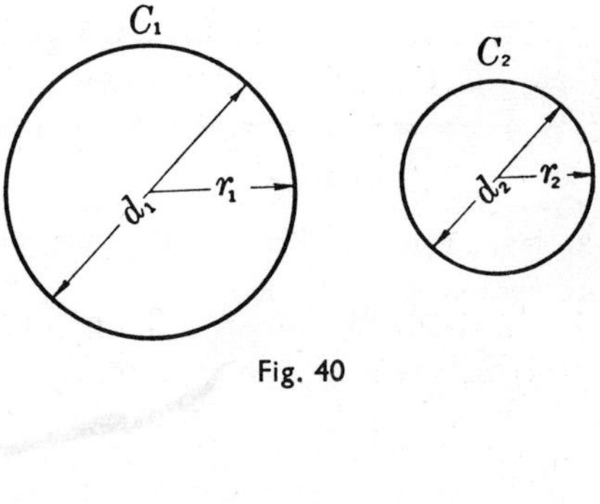

Fig. 40

Similar Rectangular Solids

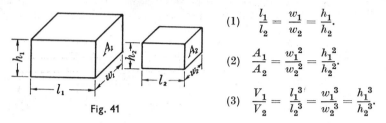

Fig. 41

(1) $\dfrac{l_1}{l_2} = \dfrac{w_1}{w_2} = \dfrac{h_1}{h_2}$.

(2) $\dfrac{A_1}{A_2} = \dfrac{w_1{}^2}{w_2{}^2} = \dfrac{h_1{}^2}{h_2{}^2}$.

(3) $\dfrac{V_1}{V_2} = \dfrac{l_1{}^3}{l_2{}^3} = \dfrac{w_1{}^3}{w_2{}^3} = \dfrac{h_1{}^3}{h_2{}^3}$.

Spheres

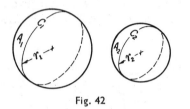

Fig. 42

(1) $\dfrac{C_1}{C_2} = \dfrac{r_1}{r_2}$.

(2) $\dfrac{A_1}{A_2} = \dfrac{r_1{}^2}{r_2{}^2}$.

(3) $\dfrac{V_1}{V_2} = \dfrac{r_1{}^3}{r_2{}^3}$.

6. If a lever is balanced on a fulcrum and supports two weights or other forces applied at points on opposite sides of the fulcrum, the weights are inversely proportional to their distances from the fulcrum (provided that the weight of the lever itself can be neglected). The three forms of the lever are illustrated in Fig. 43, in which f denotes the position of the fulcrum, W_1 and W_2 are the forces, and L_1 and L_2 are distances usually referred to as the lever arms of W_1 and W_2, respectively. In each case we have the proportion

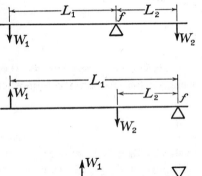

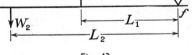

Fig. 43

$$\frac{W_1}{W_2} = \frac{L_2}{L_1}.$$

For example, suppose a uniform beam 10 ft long is supported at the middle and carries a weight of 60 lb at one end. What force must be applied at a distance of 2 ft from the other end to balance the beam?

$$\frac{W_1 \text{ lb}}{60 \text{ lb}} = \frac{5 \text{ ft}}{3 \text{ ft}}.$$

$$\frac{W_1}{60} = \frac{5}{3}.$$

$$3W_1 = 300.$$

$$W_1 = 100.$$

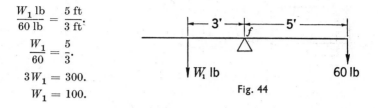

Fig. 44

7. Two pulleys connected by a belt revolve at rates that are inversely proportional to the diameters of the pulleys. In Fig. 45 d_1 and d_2 denote

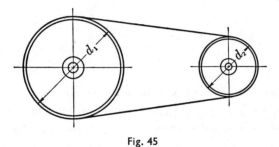

Fig. 45

the diameters of two pulleys, and R_1 and R_2 denote, respectively, their numbers of revolutions per unit of time, so that we have the proportion

$$\frac{R_1}{R_2} = \frac{d_2}{d_1}.$$

8. Two meshing gears revolve at rates that are inversely proportional to the numbers of teeth on the gears. If a gear having N_1 teeth and making R_1 rpm meshes with a gear having N_2 teeth, the number, R_2, of revolutions per minute made by the latter gear is given by the proportion

$$\frac{R_2}{R_1} = \frac{N_1}{N_2}.$$

9. If (by use of some sort of machine such as a block and tackle arrangement of pulleys) a force of F_1 lb acts through a distance of d_1 ft to

move a load of F_2 lb through a distance of d_2 ft, then, neglecting friction involved in the machine, we have the proportion

$$\frac{F_1}{F_2} = \frac{d_2}{d_1}.$$

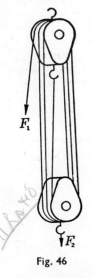

For example, if forces of friction were negligible, the arrangement of six pulleys indicated in Fig. 46 could be employed to lift a load by a force equal to one-sixth of the weight of the load. Note that the applied force F_1 would act through six times as great a distance as would the resisting force F_2. Thus, in this case

$$d_1 = 6d_2,$$

and

$$\frac{F_1}{F_2} = \frac{d_2}{6d_2}.$$

That is,

$$\frac{F_1}{F_2} = \frac{1}{6},$$

or

$$F_1 = \tfrac{1}{6}F_2.$$

Formula

Fig. 46

In forming proportions, a brief comparison of each ratio with 1 often helps the student to avoid writing an obviously false proportion in which one ratio is greater than 1 and the other is less than 1.

Problems

1. A certain triangle whose shortest side is 20 ft is similar to a triangle whose sides are 14, 10, and 8 in. Find the lengths of the other sides of the larger triangle.

2. A square whose side is 60 chains is how many times as large (in area) as a square whose side is 30 chains?

3. At the instant when the shadow of a 6-ft pole is 15 ft long, the shadow of a certain tree is 90 ft long. How high is the tree?

4. To find approximately the height of a barn a farmer sights from a point 3 ft above the ground directly over the top of a 10-ft pole to the highest point of the barn; he then measures his distance from the pole and his distance from the barn and finds them to be 8 ft and 40 ft, respectively. How high is the barn?

5. If oranges 2 in. in diameter without rind are worth 16¢ per dozen, what should be the value of oranges of the same quality 3 in. in diameter?

For Wed 15, 17, 23, 30, 42

6. If 2 cu ft of lime and 5 cu ft of sand are used in making 6 cu ft of mortar, how much of each is needed to make 63 cu ft of mortar?

7. Two machine pulleys, 20 in. and 12 in. in diameter, respectively, are connected by a belt. Find the speed of the smaller pulley when the larger is making 140 rpm. (The ratio of their speeds is equal to the inverse ratio of their diameters.)

8. Two boys, one weighing 70 lb and the other weighing 90 lb, sit at opposite ends of a 16-ft see-saw board. If the board is balanced and its weight is neglected, how far is the fulcrum from the end occupied by the larger boy?

9. The specific gravity of a substance is defined as the ratio of the weight of a given volume of that substance to the weight of an equal volume of water. If water weighs 62.5 lb per cubic foot and cement weighs 100 lb per cubic foot, what is the specific gravity of cement?

10. If an iron ball 2 in. in diameter weighs 1.1 lb, how much should a ball 6 in. in diameter weigh?

11. Neglecting the weight of the lever, find the force a man would need to apply at one end of an 8-ft crowbar to lift a weight of 390 lb situated at the other end, the fulcrum being $1\frac{1}{2}$ ft from the weight.

12. What is the ratio of the capacities of two cube-shaped boxes if the edge of the larger is twice the edge of the smaller?

13. What is the ratio of the areas of two circles if the radius of the larger is twice the radius of the smaller? What is the ratio of their circumferences?

14. An 8-ft lever whose fulcrum is at one end supports a load of 200 lb, concentrated at a point 2 ft from the fulcrum. Neglecting the weight of the lever, find the lifting force required at the other end of the lever.

15. What force is necessary to lift a weight of 840 lb by an arrangement of six pulleys in a block and tackle? What force is required if a four-pulley arrangement is used?

16. If a beef animal that is fed a daily ration of 2 lb of cottonseed meal, 10 lb of corn, and 12 lb of prairie hay gains 1.9 lb daily, how much of each of these feeds should be required to produce 100 lb of live weight? How many pounds of this feed mixture is required per pound of gain?

17. It is estimated that for hogs 4 lb of balanced feed is required per pound of gain in live weight. If hogs are fed a mixture consisting of 82% shelled corn, 5% wheat gray shorts, 9% cottonseed meal, and 4% tankage, how much of each of these feeds would be required to increase a hog's weight 100 lb?

18. In rations that contain silage, as much as half the silage may be replaced by cottonseed hulls at the rate of 2 lb of hulls to each 5 lb of silage. How many pounds of hulls would be required to make this replacement in a daily ration that includes 60 lb of silage?

19. In a ton of 3-8-4 fertilizer what is the ratio of the weight of the phosphoric acid present to the combined weight of the other plant foods present?

20. If a cow is to be fed a certain daily ration at the rate of 1 lb of feed for each 3 lb of milk produced per day, how much of this feed should be given a cow that averages $4\frac{1}{2}$ gal of 5% milk a day?

21. A motor-driven pulley 8 in. in diameter is connected by belt to a service pulley 10 in. in diameter. When the 8-in. pulley is making 120 rpm, how fast is the service pulley revolving?

22. What size service pulley should replace the one mentioned in Problem 21 if it is desirable to have the service pulley make only 80 rpm?

23. The ratio between the diameters of two circles is $\frac{1}{3}$. What is the ratio between their areas? Between their circumferences?

24. If a steel ball 4 in. in diameter weighs 9 lb, what should be the weight of a ball of similar material that measures 6 in. in diameter?

25. An edge of a certain cube-shaped box is three times as long as the edge of another cube-shaped box. The larger box will hold how many times as much as the smaller box?

26. Neglecting the weight of the lever, find the force required at a point 6 in. from one end of an 8-ft lever to balance a weight of 650 lb placed at the other end, the fulcrum being 1 ft from the weight.

27. Neglecting the weight of the lever, find the distance from one end of an 8-ft lever a force of 30 lb should be applied to balance a weight of 60 lb placed at the other end, which is $2\frac{1}{2}$ ft from the fulcrum.

28. Two horses are pulling a wagon, the total pull on the load being 300 lb. If the hitch for one of the horses is at one end of a 48-in. evener (or doubletree) and the hitch for the other horse is located 2 in. from the other end, determine the pull exerted by each of the horses. Assume that the doubletree is pivoted at its center and that the horses are kept abreast.

29. If the pulls exerted on a load by two mules should be proportional to the weights of the mules, devise a plan for properly hitching two mules, one weighing 1000 lb and the other weighing 1200 lb, to a 48-in. doubletree, which is pivoted at its center.

30. A tractor pulley that is 12 in. in diameter and turns 950 rpm is to drive an irrigation pump at 1750 rpm. About what size pulley should be used on the pump?

31. A 3-hp gas engine with a 6-in. pulley turning 500 rpm is to drive a pulley of a pump jack at 250 rpm. What size pulley is needed on the pump jack?

32. One of two meshing spur gears on adjoining shafts has 24 teeth and the other has 10 teeth. How fast is the 10-tooth gear turning when the 24-tooth gear is making 1200 rpm?

33. At what speed will a 6-in. pulley turn if it is belted to a 9½-in. tractor pulley that makes 1000 rpm?

34. A 10-in. motor-driven pulley making 800 rpm is belted to an 8-in. pulley that is on the same shaft with another 8-in. pulley, which is joined by a belt to a 12-in. machine pulley. Find the speed of the 12-in. pulley.

35. A motor making 3650 rpm has its 1¾-in. driving pulley connected with a 4-in. pulley on a lathe. Find the speed of the lathe pulley.

36. What are the lengths of the two pieces into which a stick of cord wood (4 ft) should be cut if one piece is to be 1½ times as long as the other?

37. How should a 160-acre tract of crop land be assigned to two tenant families, one furnishing 3 able workers and the other 5, if the apportioning is based upon the number of workers in a family?

38. It is estimated that about 3¾ lb of grease wool (as shorn from sheep) is required to make 1 lb of wool cloth. How many pounds of grease wool are required to furnish the cloth for a man's three-piece suit made from 3½ yd weighing 15 oz to the yard?

39. If a certain cylindrical tank is known to hold 5000 gal when full, what is the capacity of a similar tank of the same diameter and twice as tall? What is the capacity of a similar tank of the same height and with diameter twice as large?

40. About how many pounds of tension are there on a string of barbed wire when it is held taut by a 15-lb pull on the free end of a rope employed in a 4-pulley block and tackle device being used as a wire stretcher?

41. In comparing the profits to be derived from marketing corn directly and from feeding corn to hogs for market, a ratio called the hog-corn price ratio may be considered. It is defined as the number of bushels of corn whose value equals that of 100 lb of live hog weight at prevailing prices. Determine this ratio when hogs are selling at $17.55 per hundred-weight and corn is quoted at $1.35 per bushel.

42. In a certain greenhouse experiment cylindrical pots 16 in. in diameter and 12 in. tall are used. How much commercial fertilizer should be applied to the top soil in each pot to approximate a rate of distribution of 400 lb per acre?

43. How many pounds of fertilizer should be applied to a rectangular garden measuring 120 by 75 ft if the recommended rate of distribution is 800 lb per acre?

44. Two men, A and B, contract to replace a barn roof for $720.00 and agree to share one-third of the net proceeds equally and to divide the remainder in proportion to the time put in on the job. How much does each realize from the contract if $435.70 is spent for materials, a helper is employed at $6.00 per day for 5 days, and A and B work 3 days and 5 days, respectively, on the job?

CHAPTER 6

THE RIGHT TRIANGLE AND TRIGONOMETRY

Theorem of Pythagoras

Certain properties of the right triangle are involved in many problems connected with construction work. By far the most important property of the right triangle is that known as the Theorem of Pythagoras, which states that *the square of the hypotenuse is equal to the sum of the squares of the other two sides.*

Applied to triangle ACB in Fig. 47, this theorem means that

$$c^2 = a^2 + b^2,$$

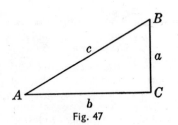

Fig. 47

where a, b, and c are the number of units in the lengths of the sides. The student may recall the proof of this theorem from his study of geometry. A few of the applications of this property are suggested in problems which follow.

Finding the Square Root of a Number

In solving problems relating to the right triangle, the student needs to know how to find the square root of a number. The method is indicated in the following examples.

Examples

1. Find the square root of 2209.

First, group the digits of the number by two's from right to left, thus:

$$\overline{22} \ \overline{09}$$

(In some cases, this procedure leaves only one digit in the group farthest to the left.)

78

Second, determine the greatest perfect square in the group of digits farthest to the left. In this case it is 16. Write down the square root of this number (in this case, 4) as the first figure of the square root. Subtract the 16 from the 22 and bring down the next group of digits in line with the remainder.

$$\begin{array}{r|l} \overline{22}\ \ \overline{09} & 4 \\ 16 \\ \hline 6\ \ 09 \end{array}$$

Third, multiply the part of the root found so far (in this case, 4) by 20 and place the product opposite the 6   09 as a trial divisor.

$$\begin{array}{r|l} \overline{22}\ \ \overline{09} & 4 \\ 16 \\ 80\ | \ \ \overline{6}\ \ \overline{09} \end{array}$$

Fourth, divide 609 by 80 and write the quotient, 7, to the right of the 4 already found. Also add a 7 to the 80 and multiply the 87 by 7.

$$\begin{array}{r|l} \overline{22}\ \ \overline{09} & 47 \\ 16 \\ 87\ |\ \ \overline{6}\ \ \overline{09} \\ 6\ \ 09 \end{array}$$

The square root of 2209 is seen to be exactly 47.

2.   Find the square root of 151.29.

Beginning at the decimal point, group digits by two's in both directions, thus:

$$\overline{1}\ \ \overline{51}\ .\ \overline{29}$$

From here on proceed as in the other example, pointing off in the square root half as many decimal places as are in the number.

$$\begin{array}{r|l} \overline{1}\ \ \overline{51}\ .\ \overline{29} & 12.3 \\ 1 \\ 22\ |\ \overline{51} \\ 44 \\ 243\ |\ \ \overline{729} \\ 729 \end{array}$$

The square root of 151.29 is 12.3. If a number is not a perfect square, its square root can be found to any number of decimal places by annexing zeros and continuing the root extraction process.

Pitch of Roof

Figure 48 indicates the meaning of certain terms and measurements used in connection with roof construction. The *pitch* of a roof is defined

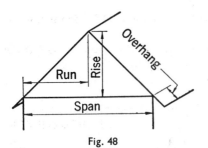

Fig. 48

as the ratio of the rise of the roof to the span, or it may be expressed as the ratio of the rise to twice the run. *Pitch* is sometimes incorrectly used as synonymous with *slope*. The *slope* of a roof is the ratio of the rise to the run.

A common rafter of a gable roof (not counting the overhang) is seen to be the hypotenuse of a right

triangle whose sides are the run and the rise of the roof. Therefore the length of such a rafter can be found by the use of the Theorem of Pythagoras if the other dimensions are known.

In actual practice a carpenter usually "steps off" the length of a rafter by placing a steel square on the side of the rafter material in such a way that 12 in. on one arm of the square corresponds to the run and a portion (depending upon the pitch) of the other arm represents the rise, and then moving the square along the piece of lumber by taking as many "steps" as there are feet in the run. By this method the markings for the top and bottom cuts on the rafter are also readily obtained.

Problems

1. There are 4840 sq yd in 1 acre. The square root of 4840, then, is the number of yards in the length of the side of a square whose area is 1 acre. Find it.

2. Find the number of rods in the side of a square containing 1 acre by extracting a square root.

3. Find the number of feet in the side of a square containing 1 acre.

4. The rectangular frame for a gate is 3 ft wide and 4 ft high. Find the length of a brace to be placed diagonally across the gate.

5. The foot of a 45-ft ladder is 27 ft from the wall of a building against which the top rests. How high does the ladder reach on the wall?

6. How many feet long is the radius of a circle whose area is 1 acre?

7. How long a guy wire is needed to reach from the top of a 40-ft pole to a point 30 ft from the foot of the pole if 1 ft is allowed at each end for fastening?

8. A baseball diamond is 90 ft square. How far is it from second base to home plate?

9. Determine the number of rods of fence required to inclose square tracts of land of the following acreages: 10, 20, 40, 60, 80, 160, 320, 640 acres.

10. How long a rafter is required for a building 36 ft wide if the rise is 12 ft and there is no overhang?

11. What length rafter would be cut for a roof whose pitch is ¼ if the roof has a span of 28 ft and an overhang of 18 in.?

The Trigonometric Ratios

In the right triangle ACB in Fig. 49 the side AB is called the *hypotenuse* of the triangle; and, with reference to angle A, the side AC is called the *adjacent side* and the side CB is called the *opposite side*. The small letters a, b, c, written on sides opposite angles lettered with corresponding capital letters, represent the measures of the lengths of those sides.

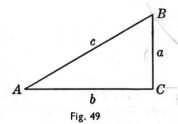

Fig. 49

It has already been stated that the size of an angle does not depend upon the lengths of the sides that form the angle. However, a very close connection exists between the size of angle A and the value of any ratio that may be formed between the lengths of two sides of the triangle. The study of these ratios and the relations they bear to the size of the angles is a part of the subject of trigonometry. In all, six distinct ratios can be formed between the lengths of the sides. They are

$$\frac{a}{c}, \quad \frac{b}{c}, \quad \frac{a}{b}, \quad \frac{c}{a}, \quad \frac{c}{b}, \quad \frac{b}{a}.$$

These ratios, of course, are abstract numbers. As a basis for identifying these ratios, names have been given to them. The first one, a/c, is called the *sine of angle A*. Using an abbreviated form, we write

$$\sin A = \frac{a}{c}.$$

Thus, *the sine of an acute angle of a right triangle is defined as the ratio of the opposite side to the hypotenuse.* The sine of angle B is of course the ratio of b to c, written

$$\sin B = \frac{b}{c}.$$

To get an idea of the relation between the size of an angle and the value of one of these ratios, let us construct a right triangle whose sides and angles are known. For convenience, draw the line segment AD two units long and then construct on AD the equilateral triangle ADB. (See Fig. 50.) Each angle of triangle ADB contains 60°. Why? Now from B drop a perpendicular BC to the base AD. This perpendicular bisects the angle at B and bisects the base, resulting in the right triangle ACB, whose angles are all known and whose sides are all known except CB. CB is at once determined by use of the Theorem of Pythagoras:

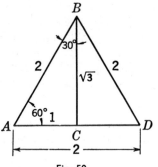

Fig. 50

$$\overline{CB}^2 + \overline{AC}^2 = \overline{AB}^2.$$

$$\overline{CB}^2 + (1)^2 = (2)^2.$$

$$\overline{CB}^2 = 4 - 1.$$

$$\overline{CB}^2 = 3.$$

$$\overline{CB} = \sqrt{3}.$$

Now from the definition for the sine of an angle,

$$\sin A = \frac{CB}{AB} = \frac{\sqrt{3}}{2}.$$

Since A is 60°, we write

$$\sin 60° = \frac{\sqrt{3}}{2}.$$

If A were an acute angle different from 60°, this ratio could not have $\sqrt{3}/2$ as its value. Furthermore, if this particular ratio had a value different from $\sqrt{3}/2$, A could not be 60°. The point to be emphasized is that the sine of an angle of a certain size has a certain definite value. Note that if an angle is 30° its sine is $\frac{1}{2}$; $B = 30°$, and $\sin B = AC/AB = \frac{1}{2}$.

The values of the other ratios are just as dependent upon the size of angle A and independent of the size of the triangle as is the sine. For this reason, they are called functions of angle A.   The ratio b/c is the cosine of angle A, written "cos A." *Thus, the cosine of an acute angle of a right triangle is defined as the ratio of the adjacent side to the hypotenuse.   The tangent of A, written "tan A," is the name given to the ratio a/b, which is the ratio of the opposite side to the adjacent side.*   Notice that the other three ratios, c/a, c/b, and b/a, are reciprocals of the three just discussed, in the order mentioned.   They are called the *cosecant of* A (csc A), the *secant of* A (sec A), and the *cotangent of* A (cot A), respectively.   We shall have occasion to use only the sine, cosine, and tangent in this course.   The student should memorize these definitions:

$$\text{Sine of an angle} = \frac{\text{side opposite the angle}}{\text{hypotenuse}}.$$

$$\text{Cosine of an angle} = \frac{\text{side adjacent to the angle}}{\text{hypotenuse}}.$$

$$\text{Tangent of an angle} = \frac{\text{side opposite the angle}}{\text{side adjacent to the angle}}.$$

By reference to the 30°, 60°, right triangle of Fig. 50 we may now write the values of the trigonometric functions of 60° and also of 30°.

Functions of 60°	*Functions of* 30°
$\sin 60° = \dfrac{\sqrt{3}}{2}$	$\sin 30° = \dfrac{1}{2}$
$\cos 60° = \dfrac{1}{2}$	$\cos 30° = \dfrac{\sqrt{3}}{2}$
$\tan 60° = \sqrt{3}$	$\tan 30° = \dfrac{1}{\sqrt{3}}$
$\csc 60° = \dfrac{2}{\sqrt{3}}$	$\csc 30° = 2$
$\sec 60° = 2$	$\sec 30° = \dfrac{2}{\sqrt{3}}$
$\cot 60° = \dfrac{1}{\sqrt{3}}$	$\cot 30° = \sqrt{3}$

Would the values of these ratios have been different if the equilateral triangle had been constructed with a side whose length was other than two units?

Every right triangle which contains a 30° angle is *similar* to triangle *ACB* of Fig. 50 and must therefore have each of the ratios between two of its sides equal to the ratio between corresponding sides of triangle *ACB*. In fact, the fundamental basis for the development of trigonometry is this principle: *All right triangles containing a common-sized acute angle are similar and therefore have their corresponding ratios between lengths of sides equal.* This fact may suggest to the student the possibility of tabulating the values of these ratios for acute angles of various sizes.

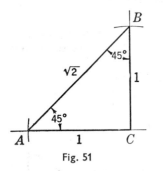

Fig. 51

Another angle whose functions can be determined by construction is an angle of 45°. At any point C on a straight horizontal line erect a perpendicular. (See Fig. 51.) Now with C as a center and a radius of 1 (any other radius might be used) swing an arc cutting the horizontal line at A and the vertical line at B. Draw AB, thereby forming a right triangle with $A = 45°$, $a = 1$, $b = 1$, and $c = \sqrt{2}$. Why is $c = \sqrt{2}$?

From the definitions of the functions, we have

$$\sin 45° = \frac{1}{\sqrt{2}} = \frac{\sqrt{2}}{2}, \text{ or } 0.707, \text{ approximately,}$$

$$\cos 45° = \frac{1}{\sqrt{2}} = \frac{\sqrt{2}}{2}, \text{ or } 0.707, \text{ approximately,}$$

and

$$\tan 45° = \frac{1}{1} = 1.$$

The student should learn to construct the two triangles just discussed and from them give the values of the functions of 30°, 45°, and 60°. In expressing these values in decimal form he will find it convenient to remember that

$$\sqrt{2} = 1.414, \text{ approximately,}$$

and

$$\sqrt{3} = 1.732, \text{ approximately.}$$

It is not possible to find the values of the trigonometric functions of all angles by geometric constructiont. However, by means of a protractor and a straight edge a fairly good drawing can be made of a right triangle which contains an acute angle of a particular size. A measuring scale can be used to determine approximately the lengths of the sides of the triangle; and the value of any function can be found approximately by forming the appropriate ratio. Such drawings should be made large enough so that measurement of the sides is practicable.

Problems

1. Draw a right triangle ACB with side a 3 in. long and side b 4 in. long. How long is side c? Give the values of sin A, cos A, and tan A. By use of a protractor find approximately the size of A. If A is known, how can B be found? Find B.

2. Draw a right triangle ACB with side $a = 12$ and the hypotenuse $c = 13$. Find b. With a protractor find A. Find B. Give the values of sin B, cos B, and tan B.

3. In Fig. 52 find by actual measurements with ruler and protractor the approximate length of each side and the size of each angle. Then give the values of the three main functions of A.

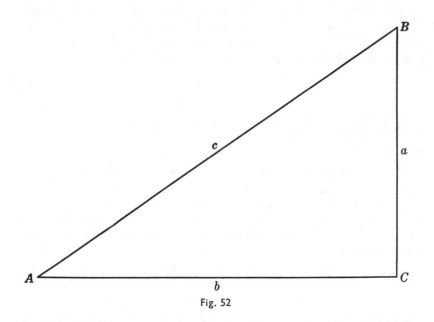

Fig. 52

4. Using a protractor and straight edge to make a suitable drawing, find approximately the values of the sine, cosine, and tangent of 52°.

5. By the method used in Problem 4, find the values of the sine, cosine, and tangent of 20°.

6. Derive the values of the sine, cosine, and tangent of 45° from a right triangle each of whose legs is 3 in. long.

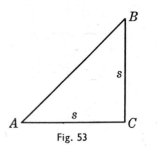

Fig. 53

7. By drawing first an equilateral triangle whose side is 5 units long, form a 60°, 30°, right triangle and derive the values of the sine, cosine, and tangent of 60°. Also give the values of these functions of 30°.

8. In Fig. 53 s is a constant representing the length of sides AC and CB. What is the size of $\angle A$? Why? Find AB in terms of s. Now find the values of the functions of 45°. Does it matter what value is given to s?

9. In Fig. 54 find a and b. *Suggestion:* $a/c = \sin 30°$. $\sin 30° = \frac{1}{2}$, and $c = 28$. Therefore $a/28 = \frac{1}{2}$, from which a is easily determined. The side b is found by using cos 30°.

10. A guy wire from the top of a pole to a point on the ground 50 ft from the foot of the pole makes an angle of 45° with the horizontal. How high is the pole? What is the length of the guy wire?

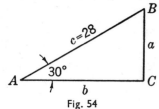

Fig. 54

Determining the Values of the Trigonometric Ratios by Line Measurement

Figure 55 may be used in determining approximately the values of the functions of an angle. The angle is formed with its vertex at A and adjacent side along AX. It may then be considered part of a right triangle whose hypotenuse is the radius of the circular arc. Since the hypotenuse AB is 100 units in length, the number of hundredths in the sine of the angle is numerically the same as the number of units in the length of the opposite side CB; and the cosine, expressed in hundredths, is numerically the same as the number of units in the length of the adjacent side AC. The tangent may be determined by dividing the opposite side by the adjacent side. The tangent can also be obtained by measurement of a single line if the right angle of the triangle is formed at C', as shown in the figure, the number of hundredths in the tangent being the same numerically as the number of units in the length of $C'B'$.

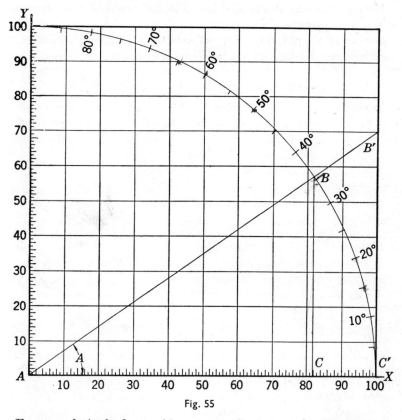

Fig. 55

For example, in the figure, A is represented as being $35°$.   We have then

$$\sin 35° = \frac{\text{Number of units in } CB}{100} = \frac{57}{100} = 0.57, \text{ approximately,}$$

$$\cos 35° = \frac{\text{Number of units in } AC}{100} = \frac{82}{100} = 0.82, \text{ approximately,}$$

and

$$\tan 35° = \frac{\text{Number of units in } CB}{\text{Number of units in } AC} = \frac{57}{82} = 0.70, \text{ approximately,}$$

or

$$\tan 35° = \frac{\text{Number of units in } C'B'}{100} = \frac{70}{100} = 0.70, \text{ approximately.}$$

(Incidentally, note that $\tan A = \sin A/\cos A$ for any angle A for which $\cos A$ is not 0.)

This diagram may also be used in estimating the size of an angle whose sine, cosine, or tangent is known.

A study of Fig. 55 will justify our extending the definitions of sin A, cos A, and tan A so that certain functions of $0°$ and $90°$ can be evaluated. Thus,

$$\sin 0° = 0 \qquad \cos 0° = 1 \qquad \tan 0° = 0$$
$$\sin 90° = 1 \qquad \cos 90° = 0 \qquad \text{(There is no tangent of } 90°)$$

It will be observed that as A approaches $90°$, tan A increases without limit.

Problems

Solve the following problems by reference to Fig. 55.

1. Determine approximately the values of the following functions: sin $20°$, cos $20°$, tan $20°$, cos $60°$, tan $50°$, sin $80°$, tan $10°$, cos $5°$, tan $65°$, sin $15°$.

2. What is the greatest value the sine of an angle can have? What is the angle whose sine has this value?

3. What is the greatest value that the cosine of an angle can have? What is the angle whose cosine has this value?

4. As an angle increases from $0°$ to $90°$ its sine increases from what value to what value?

5. As an angle increases from $0°$ to $90°$ its cosine has what range of values?

6. What range of values does the tangent of an angle have as the angle increases from $0°$ to $90°$? Note that there is no tangent of $90°$. Why?

7. Estimate the size of each of the angles represented here: sin A = 0.19, tan R = 0.49, cos M = 0.89, tan B = 1.15, sin T = 0.81.

8. If the sum of two angles is $90°$, each of the angles is said to be the complement of the other angle. What is the complement of $30°$? Compare sin $30°$ with cos $60°$.

9. Compare cos $20°$ with sin $70°$.

10. In a right triangle ACB, note that $A + B = 90°$, and therefore A and B are complementary angles. How does sin A compare with cos B? How does cos A compare with sin B?

Use of Tables

The values of most of the trigonometric functions of angles cannot be written exactly as decimal numbers. However, it is possible by methods employed in more advanced mathematics to find the value of a function to a desired number of decimal places. For convenience, tables have been made, giving the values of functions to two, three, four, five, and even more decimal places. The table to be used in any case depends upon the accuracy required.

Table XI gives to the nearest 0.0001 the values of the trigonometric ratios of angles from 0° to 90°, angles being expressed at intervals of 10 min. The entries in the table are so arranged that angles from 0° to 45° are read *down* the first column and the names of the functions are given across the *top* of the table, while angles from 45° to 90° are read *up* the last column and the names of the functions are read across the *bottom* of the table. It thus appears that each entry in the table serves as the value of two different functions. Why is such an arrangement possible? The two functions are functions of angles that are related in what way?

If an angle is expressed in greater detail than is given in the table, the value of a function of the angle can be estimated by locating the angle between two successive angles listed in the table and reasoning that the value of the required function should lie between the values of the functions of these two angles.

Examples

1. Find sin 63° 45′.

An angle of 63° 45′ is not listed in the table. It seems reasonable that sin 63° 45′ should lie about halfway between sin 63° 40′ and sin 63° 50′.

$$\sin 63° 50′ = 0.8975$$
$$\sin 63° 40′ = 0.8962$$
Differences: 10′   0.0013

An *increase* of 10′ in the angle is accompanied by an *increase* of 0.0013 in the value of the sine. Then an *increase* of 5′ in the angle should be accompanied by an *increase* in the sine of about $\frac{5}{10}$ of 0.0013, or 0.5 × 0.0013 = 0.00065, which, to four decimal places, is taken as 0.0007. Therefore, we conclude that sin 63° 45′ = 0.8962 + 0.0007 = 0.8969, approximately.

2. Find cos 27° 38′.

Cos 27° 38′ lies between cos 27° 30′ and cos 27° 40′.

$$\cos 27° 40′ = 0.8857$$
$$\cos 27° 30′ = 0.8870$$
Differences: 10′   0.0013

An *increase* of 10′ in the angle is accompanied by a *decrease* of 0.0013 in the value of the cosine. Then an *increase* of 8′ in the angle (from 27° 30′ to 27° 38′) should be accompanied by a *decrease* in the cosine of about $\frac{8}{10}$ of 0.0013, or 0.00104, which, to four decimal places, is taken as 0.0010. Hence cos 27° 38′ = 0.8870 − 0.0010 = 0.8860, approximately.

3. If tan $A = 3.0062$, what is A?

The number 3.0062 is not listed in the table as a value of the tangent. However, it lies between the two numbers 2.9887 and 3.0178, which are listed as the values of tan 71° 30′ and tan 71° 40′, respectively.

$$
\begin{array}{lll}
3.0178 = \tan\ 71°\ 40′ & & 3.0062 \\
2.9887 = \tan\ 71°\ 30′ & & 2.9887 \\
\hline
\text{Differences:}\quad 0.0291 \qquad\quad 10′ & & 0.0175
\end{array}
$$

An *increase* of 0.0291 in the tangent corresponds to an *increase* of 10′ in the angle.   Then an *increase* of 0.0175 in the tangent should correspond to an increase of approximately $\frac{0.0175}{0.0291}$ of 10′, or $\frac{175}{291} \times 10′$, which is about 6′.   Hence $A = 71° 30′ + 6′ = 71° 36′$, approximately.

Problems

Solve the following problems by reference to Table X:

1. Give the value of tan 18°, cos 5°, sin 41°, cos 32° 20′, sin 22° 50′, tan 43° 10′.

2. Give the value of sin 45°, tan 45°, cot 45°, sin 60°, tan 60°, cos 60°, cos 60° 20′.

3. Give the value of sin 68°, cos 82°, tan 76°, cos 73° 30′, sin 56° 10′, tan 45° 40′.

4. Give the value of sin 0°, sin 90°, cos 0°, cos 90°, tan 0°, tan 89°.

5. Find cos 35° 30′, sin 43° 18′, tan 12° 56′, cos 39° 7′.

6. Find tan 55° 15′, cos 57° 43′, tan 80° 19′, sin 89° 14′.

7. Find sin 34° 40′, tan 0° 54′, cos 0° 45′, sin 67° 28′.

8. Find cos 44° 25′, sin 75° 3′, cos 51° 37′, tan 89° 12′.

9. What angle has its sine equal to 0.6472?

10. If sin $A = 0.8572$, what is A?   If tan $B = 0.1673$, what is B?

11. If cos $A = 0.8718$, what is A?   If tan $R = 4.5736$, what is R?

12. Determine the angle involved in each of the following: sin $M = 0.3297$;   tan $A = 0.4428$;   cos $B = 0.4908$;   sin $A = 0.9360$; cos $D = 0.9055$.

13. A 20-ft ladder leaning against a vertical wall makes an angle of 70° 15′ with the ground.   How high up the wall does the ladder reach?

14. How long a rafter is required for a roof whose span is 30 ft if the roof makes an angle of 33° with the horizontal?

15. Note that the pitch of a roof, as previously defined, may be considered as one-half of the tangent of the angle that the roof makes with the horizontal.   For a roof whose pitch is $\frac{1}{2}$, what size is this angle?

16. About what angle does a roof whose pitch is $\frac{1}{4}$ make with the horizontal?

17. How high is a kite that is at the end of a 500-ft taut string which makes an angle of 23° 40′ with the ground?

18. From a point on the ground 40 ft from the foot of a certain tree an observer finds the angle of elevation of the top of the tree to be 50° 38′. How tall is the tree? (The angle of elevation is the angle which the line of sight makes with the horizontal.)

19. The side of a hill is inclined 6° 30′ from the horizontal. How many feet does one rise in walking 200 ft up the side of the hill?

20. In order to determine the greatest width of a lake, the measurements indicated in Fig. 56 were made. Find the width of the lake.

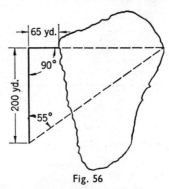

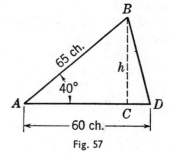

Fig. 56

21. The triangle shown in Fig. 57 is not a right triangle, but, if the altitude is dropped from B to the base, two right triangles are formed. The length, h, of altitude CB can then be determined. Find h. Find the area of the triangle.

Area of a Triangle

By the method employed in Problem 21 of the preceding group a formula can be developed for finding the area of any triangle in which two sides and the included angle are known. Consider the triangle ADB in Fig. 58, in which we may suppose that A, b, and d are known. Draw the altitude CB. Now,

$$\text{area} = \tfrac{1}{2}bh$$

and

$$\frac{h}{d} = \sin A,$$

from which

$$h = d \sin A.$$

Therefore

$$\text{area} = \tfrac{1}{2}bd \sin A.$$

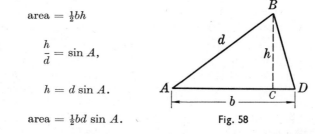

Fig. 57

Fig. 58

In the case just considered all angles of the triangle are acute. Suppose that A is obtuse, as shown in Fig. 59. Extend the base through A and draw altitude CB. Now,

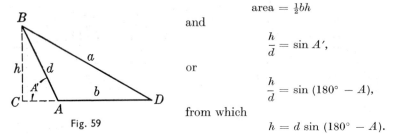

Fig. 59

and

$$\text{area} = \tfrac{1}{2}bh$$

$$\frac{h}{d} = \sin A',$$

or

$$\frac{h}{d} = \sin (180° - A),$$

from which

$$h = d \sin (180° - A).$$

Therefore, if A is obtuse,

$$\text{area} = \tfrac{1}{2}bd \sin (180° - A).$$

The angle $(180° - A)$ is called the *supplement* of angle A. In a more extensive treatment of trigonometry it is shown that the sine of an obtuse angle is the same as the sine of its supplement. That is, $\sin A = \sin (180° - A)$.

Hence the formula for the area of a triangle may be stated in words as follows:

The area of any triangle is equal to one-half the product of any two sides times the sine of their included angle.

Problems

1. Find the number of acres in the triangular plot of land represented by Fig. 60.

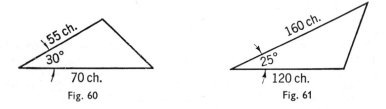

Fig. 60   Fig. 61

2. Find the area of the piece of land represented by Fig. 61.

3. Find the number of acres in the four-sided plot of land represented by Fig. 62. (*Suggestion:* Divide the quadrilateral into two triangles and measure the angles needed for use of the formula just developed.)

4. To get the area of the five-sided field represented by Fig. 63 all the angles required were read on an instrument at one corner of the field

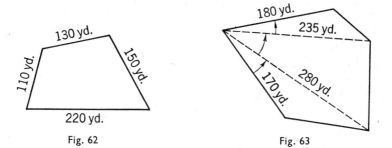

Fig. 62   Fig. 63

and then the indicated measurements of distance were made. How many acres are there in the field?

Bearing of a Line

In descriptions of tracts of land from measurements of angles and distances, the bearing (that is, the direction) of a line from a given point is expressed in terms of the acute angle that the line makes with a meridian (a north and south line) drawn through the given point. Thus in Fig. 64 the line NS is a meridian; the bearing of AB is N. 30° E., which is read "north 30° east"; the bearing of CD is S. 45° E.; that of PQ is S. 75° W.; and that of RT is N. 60° W.

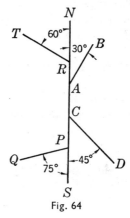

Fig. 64

Problems

1. In the following description the bearings and lengths of the boundary lines of a certain farm are given: "Beginning at a point known as the northwest corner of the tract, same being marked by a 2-in. iron pipe, and running S. 0° 50′ E. 1975 ft, thence S. 20° 30′ E. 970 ft, thence N. 77° 15′ E 1130 ft, thence N. 19° 50′ W. 475 ft, thence N. 68° E. 1255 ft, thence N. 53° 20′ W. 1635 ft, thence N. 26° 45′ E. 1810 ft, thence S. 65° 45′ W. 2150 ft to beginning corner." Using a protractor, straight edge, and measuring scale, draw a map of this farm using a scale of 1 in. to 660 ft.

2. Determine approximately the number of acres contained in the farm described in Problem 1. (The result should be about 119 acres.)

3. The boundary lines of a certain tract of land are as indicated in Fig. 65. Determine the scale used and write a description of the tract, beginning at the southwest corner, proceeding around the tract in a clockwise direction, and giving the bearing and length of each of the boundary lines.

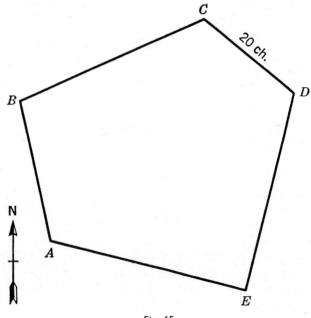

Fig. 65

4. On the farm pictured in Fig. 66, find approximately the number of acres of land in each of the fields lettered.   The scale is 1 in. to 660 ft.

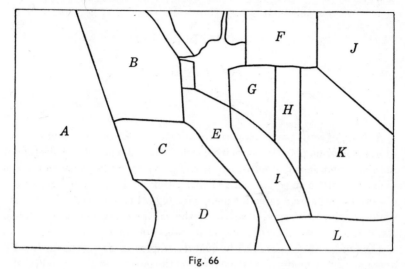

Fig. 66

5. Assuming that the diagonal from the lower right corner of Fig. 66 to the upper left corner extends due north, write a description of the tract of land pictured, indicating lengths and bearings of all boundary lines.

CHAPTER 7

AVERAGES

A study of some particular feature or attribute of an item or of a group of items may be placed on a mathematical basis if a suitable collection of numbers that serve as measures of the property under consideration is available. In connection with such a study it is usually desirable to obtain one or more numbers which, with regard to the particular feature under study, are representative of the entire collection of measures. Representative numbers of this sort are called *averages*.

The kinds of averages most frequently employed are (1) the arithmetic average, (2) the mode, (3) the median, (4) the geometric mean, and (5) the harmonic mean. The kind of average to be used in a particular case depends upon what the average is intended to show. A brief discussion of each of these averages may suggest to the student its appropriate use.

The Arithmetic Average

The arithmetic average of a collection of measures is the quotient obtained by dividing the sum of the measures by the number of measures. If some of the measures occur more than once in the collection, a distinction should be made between the *simple arithmetic mean*, in which each of the different measures is counted only once in obtaining the sum of measures, and the *weighted arithmetic mean*, in which each of the different measures is multiplied by the number of times it occurs and the sum of the products so obtained is regarded as the sum of the measures. A particular weighted arithmetic mean is equivalent to the simple arithmetic mean obtained by counting every measure as many times as it occurs in the given set of data. The averages computed in the following example illustrate appropriate uses of these two forms of the arithmetic average.

Example

A certain farmer has the following record of performance for a year on his herd of five milk cows:

Cow Number	Number of Pounds of Milk	Per Cent of Butterfat
1...........	3512	4.9
2...........	2478	4.1
3...........	9640	3.6
4...........	3250	5.4
5...........	11,265	3.5

What is the average production of milk per cow for the year?

The answer to this question is the simple arithmetic mean of the measures given in the second column. It is obtained by dividing the total number of pounds of milk by the number of cows:

$$30,145 \div 5 = 6029.$$

We may say then that this herd averaged 6029 lb of milk per cow for the year.

Next, consider the problem of finding the average per cent of butterfat in the milk produced by this group of cows. If the sum of the per cents for the individual cows is divided by 5, the result is 4.3%. Is 4.3% representative of the butterfat content of all the milk produced? Does not this figure give too much weight to the high quality of milk produced by cows 1 and 4, whose production was comparatively low, and too little consideration to the quantity of milk, testing low in butterfat, produced by cows 3 and 5? Note that the milk from these two cows made up over two-thirds of the total quantity produced and that the per cent of butterfat was 3.6 for one of them and 3.5 for the other.

Obviously, a more representative figure for the average per cent of butterfat in all of the milk would be obtained by dividing the total number of pounds of butterfat by the total number of pounds of milk. The total number of pounds of butterfat produced is the sum of the products obtained by multiplying the production of milk for each cow by the corresponding per cent of butterfat. These products are shown below.

Cow Number	Computation	Number of Pounds of Butterfat
1........	0.049 × 3512	172.088
2........	0.041 × 2478	101.598
3........	0.036 × 9640	347.040
4........	0.054 × 3250	175.500
5........	0.035 × 11,265	394.275
Total.............	30,145	1190.501

If 1190.501 is divided by 30,145, the result is approximately 0.039, or 3.9%. This average of 3.9% is a weighted arithmetic mean. It is weighted in the sense that each of the per cents given for the individual cows is multiplied by the number of pounds of milk testing that per cent. For instance, the 4.9% (for cow No. 1) is said to have a weight of 3512, since 0.049 of butterfat is contained in each pound of the 3512 lb of milk.

Computation of the arithmetic mean M of a set of n measures m_1, m_2, m_3, . . . , m_n may in some cases be shortened by selecting a number M' near which the true mean appears to be and using the relation developed in the following.

By definition,

$$M = \frac{m_1 + m_2 + m_3 + \ldots + m_n}{n}.$$

Subtracting M' from both sides, we obtain

$$M - M' = \frac{m_1 + m_2 + m_3 + \ldots + m_n}{n} - M'$$

$$= \frac{(m_1 + m_2 + m_3 + \ldots + m_n) - nM'}{n}.$$

In the preceding line, there are n terms inside the parentheses and there are the same number of M''s to be subtracted. Hence the equation can be written

$$M - M' = \frac{(m_1 - M') + (m_2 - M') + (m_3 - M') + \ldots + (m_n - M')}{n}.$$

The differences $(m_1 - M')$, $(m_2 - M')$, and so on, are readily obtained and are usually small in comparison to the measures whose average is sought. Note that the average of these differences is the difference between the true mean M and the approximate mean M'. Hence the desired mean, M, is obtained by adding to M' the average of these differences.

Example

Find the average weight per bale of 8 bales of lint cotton whose weights in pounds are 510, 495, 488, 506, 496, 525, 503, and 515.

For convenience, let $M' = 500$. Then the average of the differences, 10, -5, -12, 6, -4, 25, 3, and 15, is $\frac{38}{8}$, or $4\frac{3}{4}$. Therefore the average weight per bale for this lot of cotton is $500 + 4\frac{3}{4}$, or $504\frac{3}{4}$ lb.

handwritten: number that frequently occurs most

The Mode

The mode of a group of measures is defined as that measure which occurs most frequently. In the above example, the mode of the number of pounds of butterfat present in each pound of all the milk produced is 0.035, since 0.035 lb of butterfat is present in each of 11,265 lb of milk. In other words, we may think of the measure 0.035 as occurring 11,265 times, which is the greatest number of times any one measure occurs in the set of observations. In the popular sense, mode means fashion; and as a mathematical average it has a similar meaning, since it indicates the most usual occurrence. For example, to say that the average age at which students enter college is 18 yr means that there are more students entering college at that age than at any other age.

A given group of measures may exhibit more than one modal value. For example, in considering all the wages paid a large number of workmen engaged on a certain construction project, it might be observed that one modal wage is the most common wage paid to skilled workmen, while another modal wage is the most common wage paid to unskilled laborers.

The Median   _middle point_

The median is the middle measure of a group of measures. It is obtained by arranging the measures according to magnitude or size, counting each different measure as many times as it occurs, and then selecting the middle number of the group. In case the group contains an even number of measures, the median is the arithmetic mean of the two measures nearest the middle. In a set of observations there are just as many measures that are less than the median as there are that are greater. The example discussed above is not well adapted to showing an appropriate use of the median. The median production of milk per cow is 3512 lb; the median of the per cents of butterfat is 4.1%; but with so few observations at hand, these figures are not significant in portraying any features typical of the two groups of measures. The median is useful in situations requiring arrangement according to size.

The Geometric Mean

The geometric mean of n numbers is the nth root of the product of the numbers. For example, the geometric mean of 3, 6, 12, and 24 is

$$\sqrt[4]{3 \times 6 \times 12 \times 24}.$$

The geometric mean of two numbers, often called the *mean proportional* between the two numbers, is simply the positive square root of their product. In the proportion

$$\frac{5}{x} = \frac{x}{45}$$

x is the geometric mean of 5 and 45. Solving this equation, we have

$$x^2 = 225,$$

from which

$$x = \sqrt{225} = 15.$$

That is, 15 is *the* geometric mean between 5 and 45. Note that -15, also, is *a* geometric mean of 5 and 45.

The geometric mean is useful as an average of ratios. For example, if shelling tests on two samples of corn show that for one sample the weight of grain is $\frac{8}{9}$ of the weight of ear corn and for the other the grain weight is $\frac{49}{72}$ of that of the ear corn, the average ratio of grain weight to ear corn weight for the two kinds of corn represented by the samples may be taken as $\sqrt{\frac{8}{9} \times \frac{49}{72}}$, which is $\frac{7}{9}$. Since per cents are ratios, the geometric mean is appropriately used as an average of per cents, particularly if the facts upon which the per cents are based are not available. For example, if two investments give annual yields of 3.2% and 5%, an average yield on the two investments is $\sqrt{3.2 \times 5}\%$, or 4%.

Computation of the geometric mean of more than two measures is usually effected by means of logarithms. Since logarithms have not yet been discussed in this text, the student may at this point indicate geometric means required in problems without carrying out the actual computations.

The Harmonic Mean

The harmonic mean of a set of measures is the reciprocal of the arithmetic mean of the reciprocals of the measures. If H denotes the harmonic mean of the n measures $m_1, m_2, m_3, \ldots, m_n$, then H is given by the formula

$$\frac{1}{H} = \frac{\dfrac{1}{m_1} + \dfrac{1}{m_2} + \dfrac{1}{m_3} + \ldots + \dfrac{1}{m_n}}{n}.$$

The harmonic mean is appropriately used in averaging certain types of rates. For example, if an automobile travels a distance of 100 miles at the rate of 50 miles per hour and makes the return trip at the rate of

30 miles per hour, the average rate of speed for the entire trip is the harmonic mean of 50 and 30, and not their arithmetic mean. In this case,

$$\frac{1}{H} = \frac{\frac{1}{30} + \frac{1}{50}}{2}$$

$$= \frac{\frac{8}{150}}{2}$$

$$= \frac{4}{150}.$$

Hence

$$H = \frac{1}{\frac{4}{150}} = \frac{150}{4} = 37.5.$$

The average speed for the entire trip is 37.5 miles per hour. Note that this result is consistent with the fact that a total distance of 200 miles was traveled in $5\frac{1}{3}$ hr.

As another example of the harmonic mean, consider the average number of pounds of grain that $1 will buy if, of the only three kinds under study, one kind sells at 40 lb for $1, another sells at 25 lb for $1, and a third sells at 50 lb for $1. The arithmetic average of 40, 25, and 50 is $38\frac{1}{3}$. However, the three kinds of grain may be considered as priced at $2\frac{1}{2}c$, $4c$, and $2c$ per pound. The average of these prices is $2\frac{5}{6}c$, and at $2\frac{5}{6}c$ per pound $1 will buy $35\frac{5}{17}$ lb. This result, which seems to represent better than does $38\frac{1}{3}$ the average number of pounds purchasable at $1, is really the harmonic mean of 40, 25, and 50. Thus,

$$\frac{1}{H} = \frac{\frac{1}{40} + \frac{1}{25} + \frac{1}{50}}{3}$$

$$= \frac{\frac{5 + 8 + 4}{200}}{3}$$

$$= \frac{17}{600}.$$

Hence

$$H = \frac{600}{17} = 35\frac{5}{17}.$$

The Standard Deviation

The significance of an average of a set of measures depends upon how representative it is of the whole set—that is, whether the numbers of the set vary greatly from it or fall within a comparatively narrow range about it. Some kind of average of the variations of the measures from a mean is usually sought. The most useful average of this type is the *standard deviation*, which is defined as the square root of the arithmetic mean of the squared deviations of the measures from their arithmetic mean. If M is the arithmetic average of n measures m_1, m_2, m_3, . . . , m_n, then the standard deviation, denoted by the Greek letter sigma (σ), is given by the formula

$$\sigma = \sqrt{\frac{(m_1 - M)^2 + (m_2 - M)^2 + (m_3 - M)^2 + \ldots + (m_n - M)^2}{n}}.$$

Example

Find the standard deviation of the numbers 5, 7, 9, 12, 15, and 18.

The arithmetic mean in this case is 11, and the deviations from it are (-6), (-4), (-2), 1, 4, 7. The average of the squares of these numbers is

$$\frac{36 + 16 + 4 + 1 + 16 + 49}{6}, \text{ or } 20.3333, \text{ approximately.}$$

Hence

$$\sigma = \sqrt{20.3333} = 4.51, \text{ approximately.}$$

It should be admitted that the foregoing discussion of averages falls far short of covering the subject. Measures involved in sets of data have been treated as if they were exact, whereas, in actual practice, measures are usually approximations within certain ranges or class intervals. If a given set of measures is grouped into equally spaced class intervals and the calculation of averages is based upon the distribution of the measures over the various class intervals, methods more complex than those set forth above are required.

Problems

1. What is the average weight of 5 steers weighing 320, 516, 437, 328, and 469 lb?

2. What is the average price per dozen received for eggs if 3 doz are sold at 60¢ per dozen, 4 doz at 50¢, 7 doz at 40¢, and 2 doz at 75¢? What kind of average is this?

3. The following table shows the production of cotton for a certain year in a community comprising eight farms:

Farm Number	Number of Acres in Cotton	Total Number of Pounds of Lint Produced
1........	75	11,250
2........	43	5590
3........	6	2892
4........	180	36,900
5........	9	4077
6........	256	28,672
7........	63	8820
8........	50	6750

The average yield per acre for each farm is what kind of average? Find it for each farm.

4. The average yield per acre for the entire community in Problem 3 is what kind of average? Find it.

5. What is the average number of acres in cotton per farm in the community in Problem 3?

6. Suppose that in compliance with a program for reducing cotton acreage the following per cent reductions are made in the farms in Problem 3: farms 2, 3, and 5, 25%; farms 1, 7, and 8, 30%; and farms 4 and 6, 35%. What is the average per cent of reduction in cotton acreage in the community?

7. In a random sample from a crib of corn the lengths of 10 ears in inches are 8, 5, 7, 11, 7, 8, 9, 6, 10, and 7. What is the average length of an ear in this sample? What is the median length of ear? What is the most common, or modal length?

8. Twenty steers were grouped and bought as follows: 4 head at $80 per head, 6 head at $90, 8 head at $120, and 2 head at $135. What was the average price paid per head?

9. In 10 years a corn planter depreciated in value from $75 to $15. What was the average annual depreciation?

10. A lot of pigs were grouped and sold as follows: 8 head at $12 per head, 10 head at $15, 4 head at $18, and 3 head at $20. What was the average price per head?

11. Assuming that the letters a, b, and c have definite numerical values, write a formula (1) for their arithmetic average, (2) for their geometric mean, and (3) for their harmonic mean.

12. In a class of 23 students, the following grades were made in a certain subject: two A's, eight B's, six C's, four D's, two E's, and one F. What was the median letter grade obtained?

13. Assuming that the letter grades mentioned in Problem 12 have definite numerical values, write a formula for the average grade.

14. A farmer has the following record on the yield of lint from 5 bales of seed cotton:

Bale Number	Pounds of Seed Cotton	Pounds of Lint Cotton
1........	1640	523
2........	1625	512
3........	1575	508
4........	1600	500
5........	1530	490

Determine the per cent yield of lint for each bale and the average per cent yield of lint for the five bales.

15. If the total amount received for the 5 bales of cotton mentioned in Problem 14 was $886.55, what was the average price received per bale? What was the average price received per pound of lint?

16. What is the average price per pound received for cotton if one 490-lb bale is sold at 30¢ per pound, two 510-lb bales are sold at 34¢ per pound, and three 500-lb bales are sold at 38¢ per pound? What is the average price received per bale?

17. What was the average price received per dozen for eggs if 9 doz were sold at 60¢ per dozen, 12 doz were sold at 54¢, 21 doz were sold at 45¢, and 6 doz were sold at 70¢?

18. What was the average price received per dozen for eggs if 8 doz were sold at 40¢ per dozen, 5 doz were sold at 35¢, 7 doz were sold at 30¢, and 12 doz were sold at 28¢?

19. What is the average price paid per pound of plant food nutrient if 3 tons of a 2-8-4 fertilizer are bought at $36 per ton?

20. What is the average price paid per hundredweight for cottonseed meal if 2 tons are bought at $80 per ton, 1 ton is bought for $72, and 3 tons are bought at $64 per ton?

21. On a certain construction job 5 men each receive a daily wage of $5.00, 6 men each receive $7.20, 8 men each receive $9, and 1 man receives $12. What is the average daily wage per man on this job?

22. What is the average price per pound received for a 300-lb beef carcass if 10% of it is sold at 75¢ per pound, 18% at 96¢, 24% at 90¢, 22% at 66¢, 14% at 54¢, 9% at 45¢, and 3% at 30¢?

23. What was the average price per pound received by a farmer for potatoes if he sold 18 bu at $2.50 per bushel, 12 bu at $3.20 per bushel, and 1500 lb at 3½¢ per pound?

24. What was the average price per quart received by a dairyman for milk if he sold 12 gal at 60¢ per gallon, 75 qt at 20¢ per quart, 40 pt at 12¢ per pint, and 24 half-pints at 7¢ per half-pint?

25. A man accepted a job on January 1 of a certain year at $250 per month, payable at the end of the month. After 3 months his salary was increased by $25 per month; at the end of the next 3 months he received an additional increase of $15 per month; and at the end of each 2 months thereafter he received a further increase of $10 per month. How much did he receive for his work in December of that year? What was his average monthly salary for the year?

26. A group of 5 men worked 12 days of 8 hr each on a certain job at 75¢ an hour and 18 days at 90¢ an hour. A group of 7 men working on the same job received $10 per day per man during the first 12 days and $12 per day per man during the next 18 days. What was the average amount received per hour by a man on this job during the 30-day period?

27. Find the geometric mean of 2 and 8.

28. Find the geometric mean of $6\frac{3}{4}$ and 12.

29. Find the geometric mean of 2, $5\frac{1}{3}$, and 6.

30. Find the geometric mean of 3, 6, 8, and 9.

31. During a certain year the prices of three basic commodities increased 3%, 8%, and 9% of their respective average prices for the preceding year. Determine the average per cent of increase in price for these commodities as indicated by a geometric mean.

32. It is estimated that during the first year of its use a certain machine depreciates 16% of its cost value and during the second year it depreciates 9% of the value that it had at the beginning of that year. Find as a geometric mean an average annual per cent of depreciation.

33. The numerical grades made by a class of 20 students in a certain course were 86, 82, 70, 65, 75, 70, 95, 68, 77, 77, 72, 65, 73, 77, 84, 67, 55, 76, 88, and 76. Find the median grade and use it in determining the range of grades to be designated by the letter C if this median grade is also the median of the C's and 50% of all the grades are to be C's.

34. Show that the harmonic mean H of two numbers a and b is given by the formula $H = 2ab/(a + b)$.

35. Show that the harmonic mean H of three numbers, a, b, and c is given by the formula $H = 3abc/(ab + ac + bc)$.

36. On one occasion a farmer plows a field of 20 acres at the rate of $1\frac{1}{4}$ acres per hour, and during a second plowing he averages $2\frac{1}{2}$ acres per hour. What is his average rate of plowing in acres per hour?

37. A man travels a distance of 300 miles by train at an average rate of 40 miles per hour and returns an equal distance by automobile at an average rate of 50 miles per hour. What was his average rate of travel for the whole trip?

38. On the basis of average prices of fertilizer materials for a certain year it is estimated that $1 will buy 8 lb of nitrogen or 12 lb of phosphoric acid or 16 lb of potash. What is the average number of pounds of plant food that $1 will buy?

39. Find to two decimal places the standard deviation of the following numbers of pounds in the weights of ten 1-bu baskets of wheat: 58, 60, 61, 59, 61, 62, 60, 59, 61, 59.

40. Laboratory tests on eight samples of cottonseed meal supposed to contain 43% protein showed their protein contents by per cents to be as follows: 42.6, 43.0, 41.8, 43.6, 44.0, 43.2, 43.8, 42.8. Find the standard deviation of these measures.

41. The number of cattle on feed in the United States on January 1 of each year from 1946 to 1950 is shown in the following table.

	1946	1947	1948	1949	1950
No. of cattle (1000 head) ..	4,211	4,307	3,821	4,530	4,552

Find the average number of cattle on feed at the beginning of a year during this period.

42. The following table gives the number of pigs produced in the United States during each of the years shown.

	1946	1947	1948	1949	1950
No. of pigs (thousands) ..	82,940	84,147	85,187	95,688	99,079

Find the average annual pig crop for this period.

43. The number of horses and mules on farms in the United States on January 1 of certain successive years was as follows.

	1945	1946	1947	1948	1949	1950
No. of animals (thousands)..	11,950	11,063	10,021	9,130	8,246	7,463

Find the average annual decrease in the number of horses and mules for this period.

44. For the period here shown find the average annual increase in the number of tractors on farms in the United States.

	1945	1946	1947	1948	1949	1950
No. of tractors (thousands)..	2,422	2,585	2,800	3,150	3,500	3,825

45. From the following data find the average number of workers on farms in the United States during the period 1945–1950.

	1945	1946	1947	1948	1949	1950
Farm workers (thousands)..	10,813	11,092	11,166	11,080	10,756	10,455

46. Find the average value of farm real estate in the United States during the period shown.

	1943	1944	1945	1946	1947	1948	1949	1950
Farm real estate ($ billion)	37.9	42.5	46.4	52.1	58.6	62.8	65.2	63.5

47. Of 18 beef calves weighing 8420 lb, three small ones weighed 385, 405, and 455 lb, respectively. Find the average weight of the other 15 calves.

48. Cottonseed production in the United States and throughout the world for the years 1945–1949 is here given.

	1945	1946	1947	1948	1949
U.S. production (1000 tons)	3,664	3,514	4,682	5,945	6,613
World production (1000 tons)	9,980	10,270	11,680	13,355	14,425

Find the average annual production of cottonseed in the United States for this period.

49. From data in the preceding problem find the average annual world production of cottonseed for the period 1945–1949.

50. A male beef calf of desirable type weighs about 80 lb at birth and may be expected as a well-fed steer to weigh 450 lb at 6 months, 850 lb at 12 months, 1100 lb at 18 months, 1300 lb at 24 months, and 1475 lb at 30 months. Find the average increase in weight per day during the period of greatest gain and during the period of least gain.

51. A 1200-lb grain-fed steer can be expected to lose in shipment about 20 lb for the first 50 miles, 30 lb for the first 100 miles, 40 lb for the first 400 miles, and 50 lb for the first 1000 miles. Find the average loss in weight per mile of shipment for each of these distances.

52. On a certain day, a milk distributor bought 1250 lb of milk testing 4.2% butterfat, 980 lb testing 3.5%, 1025 lb testing 3.8%, and 420 lb testing 4.5%. Find the average per cent of butterfat in the milk bought that day.

CHAPTER 8

GRAPHS

It is often desirable to use diagrams or scaled drawings to present quickly and forcefully the main facts indicated by a collection of data. Such drawings are commonly called *graphs*. The student has met with many graphical presentations of statistics in his study of geography and other subjects and also in present-day newspapers and magazines. The kinds of graphs most frequently used are bar graphs, area charts, and rectangular coördinate, or line, graphs.

Bar Graphs

The *bar graph* of a set of data is simply a set of line segments or bars whose lengths are proportional to the measures they represent. In constructing a bar graph, a correspondence is first set up between a unit of length of the bar and some definite measure used in the data to be presented. Bar graphs are particularly useful in exhibiting comparisons between measures of items of the same kind.

As an example of the use of the bar graph, consider the data in the accompanying table.

DAILY WATER REQUIREMENTS OF ANIMALS

Animal	Gallons of Water per Day
Horse.	9
Cow.	$8\frac{1}{2}$
Hog.	$2\frac{1}{2}$
Sheep.	$1\frac{1}{2}$

If we let 1 in. represent 2 gal of water, these data may be exhibited graphically as shown in Fig. 67.

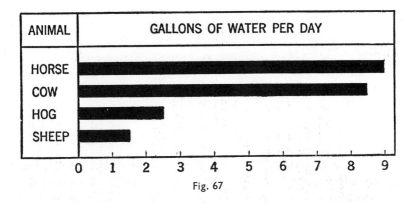

Fig. 67

The cumulative type of bar graph, in which each bar is made up of sections that correspond to parts that make up the measure represented by the whole bar, is illustrated by Fig. 68. The following data was used in making this set of bar graphs.

ANNUAL PIG CROP, BY REGIONS, UNITED STATES, 1924-1939
(in thousands)

Year	Eastern Corn Belt	Western Corn Belt	Total Corn Belt	Other States	United States Total
1924.....	18,512	39,128	57,640	16,425	74,065
1925.....	17,433	35,955	53,388	16,922	70,310
1926.....	18,428	38,704	57,132	18,312	75,444
1927.....	20,015	40,236	60,251	20,995	81,246
1928.....	18,974	40,382	59,356	19,326	78,682
1929.....	18,247	40,229	58,476	17,649	76,125
1930.....	17,881	40,025	57,906	16,229	74,135
1931.....	19,886	44,651	64,537	18,639	83,176
1932.....	21,836	39,487	61,323	21,202	82,525
1933.....	23,022	40,670	63,692	20,508	84,200
1934.....	15,445	25,025	40,470	16,296	56,766
1935.....	15,442	22,646	38,088	16,998	55,086
1936.....	18,081	26,376	44,457	20,460	64,917
1937.....	17,860	23,581	41,441	20,466	61,907
1938.....	20,106	27,866	47,972	23,129	71,101
1939.....	23,478	34,312	57,790	26,538	84,328

The following interpretation of this graph is given in the 1941 Agricultural Outlook Chart on Livestock, published by the Bureau of Agricultural Economics, United States Department of Agriculture:

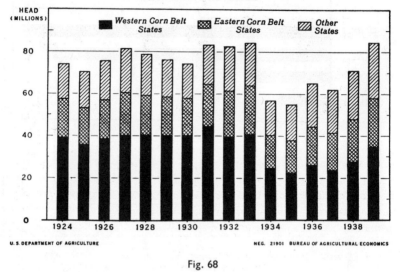

Fig. 68

During the 10 years prior to 1934 the annual pig crop of the United States averaged about 78 million head, of which nearly 75 per cent was produced in the Corn Belt States. Because of drought conditions in 1934 which greatly curtailed corn production, the pig crops of 1934 and 1935 were greatly reduced. Some increase occurred in 1936 but dry weather again in that year caused another reduction in the pig crop in 1937. With the return of normal weather conditions and increased feed production in the Corn Belt, pig crops have again increased. The 1939 pig crop of 84.3 million head was the largest on record. Since late 1939, however, hog prices have been low relative to the price of corn, and this has been reflected in reduced pig crops in all regions of the United States in 1940.

Modifications of the bar graph are sometimes made by having the bars associated with pictures suggestive of the items represented. Such modifications tend to make the presentation more vivid and effective, as will be seen from Figs. 69 and 70, which appeared in the 1951 issue of Agricultural Outlook Charts published by the Bureau of Agricultural Economics, U.S. Department of Agriculture.

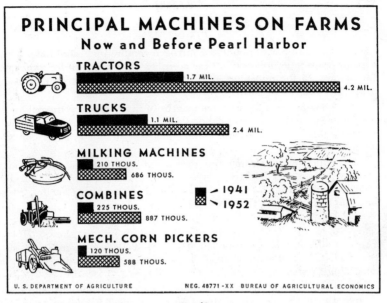

PRINCIPAL MACHINES ON FARMS
Now and Before Pearl Harbor

TRACTORS
1.7 MIL.
4.2 MIL.

TRUCKS
1.1 MIL.
2.4 MIL.

MILKING MACHINES
210 THOUS.
686 THOUS.

COMBINES
225 THOUS.
887 THOUS.

1941
1952

MECH. CORN PICKERS
120 THOUS.
588 THOUS.

U. S. DEPARTMENT OF AGRICULTURE   NEG. 48771 - XX BUREAU OF AGRICULTURAL ECONOMICS

Fig. 69

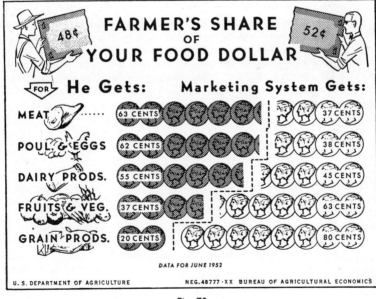

FARMER'S SHARE
OF
YOUR FOOD DOLLAR

48¢   52¢

FOR   He Gets: Marketing System Gets:

	He Gets	Marketing System Gets
MEAT	63 CENTS	37 CENTS
POUL. & EGGS	62 CENTS	38 CENTS
DAIRY PRODS.	55 CENTS	45 CENTS
FRUITS & VEG.	37 CENTS	63 CENTS
GRAIN PRODS.	20 CENTS	80 CENTS

DATA FOR JUNE 1952

U. S. DEPARTMENT OF AGRICULTURE   NEG. 48777 - XX BUREAU OF AGRICULTURAL ECONOMICS

Fig. 70

For Friday Nov. 17

Problems

1. The number of pounds of nitrogen required per acre for producing certain crops is as follows: 10 for corn, 12 for wheat, 40 for cabbage, 45 for onions, 15 for radishes, 30 for potatoes, 5 for beans. Prepare a bar graph showing these data.

2. The approximate average lengths of fibers of the principal kinds of cotton are as follows: Sea Island, 1.61 in.; Egyptian, 1.41 in.; American Upland, 0.93 in.; American long-staple, 1.3 in. Prepare a bar graph showing these data.

3. Following are some top records of butterfat production in one year by dairy cows of different breeds: Holstein-Friesian 1402 lb, Ayrshire 1356 lb, Jersey 1313 lb, Guernsey 1213 lb, Brown Swiss 1200 lb. Prepare bar graphs comparing these records.

4. During the period 1931–1940 the average number of pure-bred dairy cattle registered annually in certain breeds was as follows: Holstein-Friesian 90,598, Guernsey 44,650, Jersey 43,950, Ayrshire 13,016, Brown Swiss 6610. Construct a chart of bar graphs comparing these registrations according to breed.

5. Dressing per cents for certain types of beef animals range about as follows: good type show steers 59 to 63, good to choice grade steers 56 to 59, fat cows 54 to 58, canners 35 to 43. Prepare a chart of double bars to show these ranges, one bar of each pair representing the lower dressing per cent and the other the higher dressing per cent.

6. The improvement of swine herds by use of pure-bred boars is indicated in the following experimental data by the number of pounds of feed required per 100 lb of live weight gain made by hogs of different breeding: scrubs 465 lb, 50% purebred 403 lb, 75% purebred 388 lb, and 87.5% purebred 382 lb. Make bar graphs exhibiting these facts.

7. Distribution of the cotton supply in the United States for certain years is given in the following table.

Year	Total Supply (1000 bales)	Mill Consumption (1000 bales)	Exports (1000 bales)	Carry-over Stocks (1000 bales)
1925	18,093	6,506	8,045	3,542
1935	17,835	6,386	6,040	5,409
1945	20,362	9,423	3,613	7,326

Exhibit these data by means of bar graphs, constructing a bar for each year's total supply and dividing each bar proportionately to show the proper distribution for that year.

8. Distribution of domestically used wheat for certain years is here given.

Year	Total Supply (million bu)	Human Food (million bu)	Animal Feed (million bu)	Seed (million bu)	Industrial (million bu)
1943	1,216.0	543.1	488.1	77.3	107.5
1945	895.4	488.5	303.9	82.0	21.0
1947	769.2	498.0	179.2	91.4	0.6

Prepare bar graphs showing these data, constructing a bar for each year's

total supply and dividing it proportionately according to the distribution
for that year.

9. The annual production of cottonseed by the United States and
by the world for certain years is given in the following table.

Cottonseed Production	Average 1935–39	1945	1946	1947	1948	1949
United States (1000 short tons)......	5,554	3,664	3,514	4,682	5,945	6,613
World (1000 short tons)......	15,295	9,980	10,270	11,680	13,355	14,425

Show these data by means of bar graphs, making a bar of proper length
to represent each annual world production and shading a lower portion
of each bar to indicate that year's production by the United States.

10. In the following table the annual production of peanuts by the
United States and by the world is given for certain years.

Peanut Production	Average 1935–39	1945	1946	1947	1948	1949
United States (1000 short tons)......	614.7	1,021.1	1,019.2	1,091.4	1,169.2	937.9
World (1000 short tons)..	9,550	9,607	10,582	10,774	11,025	11,800

Construct bar graphs, similar to those of the preceding problem, showing
the relation of peanut production in the United States to that of the world
for the years shown.

11. From the following data prepare a chart of bar graphs, similar to
those of Problem 9 of this group, to show the relation of annual soybean
production in the United States to the total world production for the
several years shown.

Soybean Production	Average 1935–39	1945	1946	1947	1948	1949
United States (1000 short tons)....	1,687	5,768	6,044	5,512	6,697	6,676
World (1000 short tons)....	13,943	15,300	16,538	16,126	16,883	15,228

12. The disposition of the cotton supply in the United States for certain
years is given in the following table.

Cotton Supply	1925	1930	1935	1940	1945
Consumption (million bales)..	6.6	5.4	6.6	9.6	9.6
Exports (million bales)..	9.3	7.8	5.7	2.9	3.0
Carry-over (million bales)..	2.9	6.8	5.6	11.1	7.0
Total.......	18.8	20.0	17.9	23.6	19.6

Make a chart of bar graphs to show these data, constructing a bar to
represent the total supply for each year and dividing the bar into parts
proportional to the consumption, exports, and carry-over for that year.

13. The accompanying table gives the production per capita and the consumption per capita of meat in certain countries for the year 1949.

Per Capita	Argentina*	Australia	Canada	Denmark	New Zealand	United Kingdom	United States
Production (pounds)......	300	288	144	210	614	40	146
Consumption (pounds)......	229	217	133	136	206	92	144

* Excludes farm production and consumption of pork.

Prepare a chart of double bars to show these data, one bar of each pair to represent the per capita production for a country and the other bar to represent the per capita consumption for that country.

14. The annual production of carcass meat by the United States and by the world for certain years appears in the following table.

Production	Average 1934–38	1944	1945	1946	1947	1948	1949*
United States (million pounds)	16,182	25,178	23,687	22,596	23,430	21,596	21,879
World (million pounds)	67,900	66,100	60,800	61,900	65,500	64,700	68,300

* Preliminary estimate.

Construct a chart of bar graphs showing the relation of U.S. production to world production with each bar representing world production for a year, and its shaded lower portion representing U.S. production for that year.

15. Using data from Table VII, make bar graphs showing the plant food nutrients contained in one acre yield of cotton (lint and seed), corn (grain), tobacco (leaves), wheat (grain and straw), oats (grain and straw), and cow peas, the bar for each crop consisting of three portions that represent in order the number of pounds each of nitrogen, phosphoric acid, and potash.

16. In processing, a ton of cottonseed yields about 900 lb of meal, 550 lb of hulls, 300 lb of oil, and 118 lb of lint. Considering the rest of the ton as waste matter, construct a single bar graph, properly divided, to show this breakdown of cottonseed into its component products.

Area Charts

Area charts or graphs employ areas in much the same way that lengths are used in bar graphs. A correspondence is set up between a unit of area and a common measure used in the table of data, and areas are then formed proportional to the measures being represented. The two figures most often used in exhibiting areas are the rectangle and the sector of a circle.

In an area chart consisting of rectangles, the rectangles are usually made to have equal widths, the variations in length being proportional to the measures represented. If areas of squares are employed to represent a set of measures, the lengths of the sides of the squares are proportional to the square roots of the measures represented. Comparisons of areas of squares from their appearance are usually misleading, and therefore this type of area chart is seldom used.

The areas of sectors of the same circle are particularly well adapted to showing the relation between the measure of a total quantity of some kind and the measures of the various parts which make up the total. Since the areas of sectors of the same circle are proportional to the sizes of the central angles, circular graphs or charts are easily made by simply laying off at the center of a circle angles that are proportional to the measures represented. The size of the angle to be used for any particular measure is obtained by multiplying the ratio of the particular measure to the total of the measures by 360°. That is,

$$\text{Angle} = \frac{\text{Particular measure}}{\text{Total of measures}} \times 360°.$$

If the per cent that a particular measure is of the whole quantity represented is known, then the vertical angle of the corresponding sector is simply that per cent of 360°. The vertical angles of the sectors are easily laid off by means of a protractor.

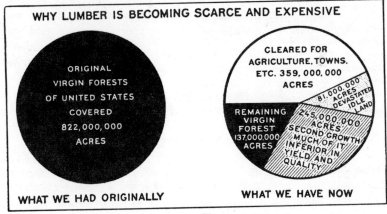

Fig. 71

Figure 71 is a circular area chart which appeared in a yearbook of the United States Department of Agriculture. The angles required in dividing the circular area into sectors are shown in the accompanying table.

Distribution	Millions of Acres	Angle of Sector
Original virgin forests	822	360°
Cleared for agriculture, towns, etc.....	359	157.2°
Second growth	245	107.3°
Virgin forests left.................	137	60°
Devastated	81	35.5°

Figure 72 is an illustration of the effective use of a circular chart to emphasize the importance of the dairy industry in the United States.

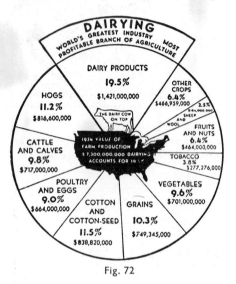

Fig. 72

The diagram shown in Fig. 73 appeared in a United States Department of Agriculture yearbook. A similar chart might be made showing the distribution of the consumer's dollar in the purchase of any commodity concerning which statistics are available.

Figure 74 consists of a series of circular charts showing for three successive periods the origin of world exports of grain and grain products. Note the effective emphasis given to the increase of grain exports from the United States. Also, observe that the sizes of the circles are proportional to the total exports for the periods shown.

Problems

1. The per cent of the carcass weight in various cuts of beef is as follows: ribs, 9.5; loin, 18; round, 24; chuck, 22; plate, 14.5; flank and shank, 9; kidney suet, 3. Prepare a circular area chart showing these data.

2. The percentage composition of potatoes is as follows: water, 75; starch, 18; sugar, 3; proteins, 2; fat, 0.2; salts, 0.7; waste material, 1.1. Prepare a circular area chart showing these data.

3. The per cent of the carcass weight in various cuts of pork is as follows: loin, 14; shoulder, 9; shoulder butts, 7; spareribs, 2; ham, 21;

bacon, 15; lard, 12; neck and feet, 4; trimmings, 13; waste, 3. Prepare an area chart showing these data.

4. Figure 75 shows the relative value of certain field crops in the United States in a certain year. Determine approximately the per cent that the value of each crop was of the value of all crops, using a protractor to measure the angles of sectors.

5. The percentage composition of a fresh-laid egg is as follows: shell, 11.4; other ash, 0.8; protein, 13.2; fat, 8.9; water, 65.7. Prepare an area chart showing these data.

6. The percentage composition of wheat grain is as follows: water, 10.5; ash, 1.8; protein, 11.9; crude fiber, 1.8; nitrogen-free extract, 71.9; fat, 2.1. Prepare an area chart showing these data.

DIVISION OF CONSUMER'S DOLLAR
BEEF AND BY-PRODUCTS
CALCULATED AS OF JUNE.1921

Fig. 73

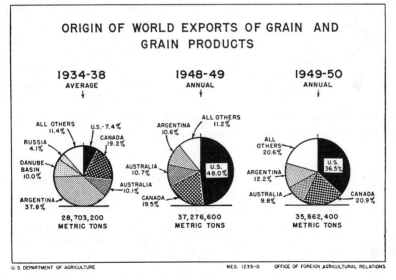

ORIGIN OF WORLD EXPORTS OF GRAIN AND GRAIN PRODUCTS

1934-38 AVERAGE	1948-49 ANNUAL	1949-50 ANNUAL

28,703,200 METRIC TONS   37,276,600 METRIC TONS   35,862,400 METRIC TONS

U. S. DEPARTMENT OF AGRICULTURE   NEG. 1235-0   OFFICE OF FOREIGN AGRICULTURAL RELATIONS

Fig. 74

7. The acreages seeded to wheat in 1939 in the four main wheat-producing regions of the United States were estimated as follows: hard winter wheat region, 28,306,000; spring wheat region, 17,034,000; soft red winter wheat region, 11,965,000; Pacific Northwest, 3,741,000. Exhibit these data by use of rectangular area charts, first with rectangles of equal length and then with squares. On which of these two types of rectangular area charts are comparisons more easily made?

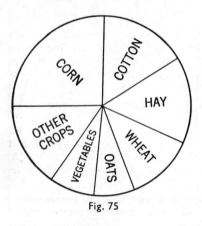

Fig. 75

8. It has been estimated that the total land area of 1,903,000,000 acres in the United States is distributed about as follows: improved land, 503,000,000 acres; forest (including cut-over and burnt-over land), 465,000,000 acres; unimproved pasture and range land, 863,000,000 acres; nonagricultural land, 72,000,000 acres. Exhibit these data (a) by use of one large rectangle divided into appropriate parts, and (b) by use of circular sectors of a circle. Which of the two charts is the more readily interpreted?

9. For a certain year it was estimated that about 40% of all the corn produced in the United States was fed to hogs on farms, 20% was fed to horses and mules on farms, 15% was fed to cattle on farms, 4% was fed to poultry, 3.5% was used for human food on farms, 5.5% was fed to livestock not on farms, 6.5% was ground in merchant flour mills, 1.5% was exported, and 4% was used in various other ways. Prepare a circular area chart showing these data.

10. In 1938 about 21.1% of the corn exports from the United States went to the United Kingdom, 10.6% went to Germany, 39.4% went to Canada, 13.6% went to the Netherlands, 2.1% went to Denmark, and 13.2% went to other foreign countries. Prepare an area chart showing these data.

11. A certain family's annual income is expended about as follows: rent, $480; food, $600; transportation, $360; clothing, $270; insurance and other savings, $315; recreation, $120; care of health, $90; other expenditures, $165. Show the distribution of these expenditures by use of sectors of a circle.

12. The weights of the wholesale cuts of an open side of beef weighing 291 lb are about as follows: round and rump, 62 lb; rib, 65 lb; loin, 30 lb; chuck, 58 lb; flank, $9\frac{1}{2}$ lb; plate, $20\frac{1}{4}$ lb; brisket, $21\frac{3}{4}$ lb; fore shank, $22\frac{3}{4}$ lb; loss in cutting, $1\frac{1}{4}$ lb. Exhibit these data by use of circular sectors.

13. A lamb carcass is usually divided into wholesale cuts about as follows: legs 33%, loin and flank 17%, hotel rack 12%, chuck (including neck) 23.5%, and breast (including shank) 14.5%. Find the weight of each of these cuts obtained from a 75-lb lamb which dresses 48%, and make a circular sector chart showing this distribution of the lamb carcass.

14. A moderately fat hog weighing 162 lb at time of slaughter yields about 154 lb of body substance, consisting of the following components: water 75.8 lb, protein 21.1 lb, fat 52.7 lb, and ash 4.4 lb. Compute the per cent of body substance in each of these components and make a circular chart to show this analysis of body substance.

15. For the period 1934–1938 the average annual world production of 68.1 billion lb of meat may be classified by types about as follows: beef and veal 49.0%, pork 41.1%, mutton and lamb 9.1%, and other kinds 0.8%. For the year 1949 the 68.3 billion lb produced consisted of these types: beef and veal 52.1%, pork 37.8%, mutton and lamb 8.8%, and other kinds 1.3%. Make a two-circle chart showing these divisions of meat production according to types.

16. The consumer's dollar spent in New York in 1949 for southeastern early Irish potatoes was distributed about as follows: grower 35.2¢, retailer 32.2¢, wholesaler 6.3¢, transportation 14.2¢, and shipping point charges including harvesting, grading, packaging, etc. 12.1¢. Construct a circular sector chart to show this distribution of the consumer's potato dollar.

17. Records indicate that the consumer's dollar paid for tomatoes produced in South Carolina and marketed in New York in 1948 was distributed about as follows: farm production 31.3¢, assembling and packing 12.4¢, transportation 8.9¢, cost of first sale (commission and other services) 8.1¢, wholesaler and retailer handling 39.3¢. Construct a circular sector chart to show this disposition of the consumer's tomato dollar.

18. The 22,298,000 tons of poultry and livestock feed shipped from plants in the United States in 1947 consisted of the following kinds of feed: dairy feed 5,272,000 tons, pig and hog feed 1,478,000 tons, feed for beef cattle, sheep, and goats 507,000 tons, horse and mule feed 534,000 tons, poultry feeds 10,887,000 tons, other feeds 3,620,000 tons. Make a circular sector chart showing this division of feed into the various kinds.

19. The total value of poultry products produced in the United States in 1949 was estimated at $3.5 billion, divided on the basis of values as follows: eggs 60%, farm produced chickens 19%, broilers 12%, turkeys 8%, and other products 1%. Construct a circular sector chart showing the breakdown of this $3.5 billion into the values of the various poultry products.

20. For the 1948–1949 turkey season a dollar paid by the consumer for turkey was distributed among the various services involved about as follows: farm production 78.9¢, assembling and processing 5.3¢, inter-market transportation 4.3¢, wholesaling 1.0¢, and retailing 10.5¢. Show this distribution of the consumer's turkey dollar by means of a circular sector chart.

21. In the following table on the origin of world exports of grain and grain products, the average year's exports are given for the prewar period 1934–1938, along with the year's exports for the 1949–1950 season.

Exports Average	Argentina	Australia	Canada	Danube Basin	Russia	United States	All Others
1935–38 (1000 metric tons)..	10,851	2,910	5,496	2,878	1,172	2,112	3,284
1949–50 (1000 metric tons)..	4,360	3,525	7,521	*	*	13,076	7,380

* Exports small and included in the "All others" entry.

Prepare a chart consisting of two circles whose areas are proportional to the total yearly exports for the two periods, with each circle divided into sectors of appropriate sizes. (Compare your chart with that of Fig. 74.)

22. For the period 1936–1940 the average yearly exports of rice totaled about 8.6 million short tons with origins about as follows: Burma 38%, Siam 18%, Indochina 17%, Korea 15%, Formosa 5%, and other countries 7%. The average annual imports totaling 8.1 million short tons for that period were distributed about as follows: Japan 24%, Europe 18%, India 15%, Ceylon 7%, British Malaya 8%, other Asiatic countries 12%, Western Hemisphere 5%, and other countries 11%. Prepare a chart of two circles properly divided to show these facts.

23. Significant changes in production costs on family-operated farms are indicated by the following estimates of the share of the gross-income dollar going for this purpose on several types of farms for the period 1935–1939 and the year 1947.

Type of Farm	Production Costs Average 1935–39	1947
Hog and beef fattening (Corn Belt region).....	47¢	27¢
Dairying (Central New York)...............	56¢	48¢
Winter wheat (Southern Plains)............	54¢	13¢
Cotton (Black Prairie)....................	36¢	33¢
Cotton (Southern Plains)..................	38¢	27¢

Construct a pair of circular charts for each type of farm, shading the "farm cost sector" of each circle.

Rectangular Coördinate Graphs

The *rectangular coördinate graph*, or *line graph*, as it is often called, usually consists of a line or curve drawn through certain points whose positions are determined by the measures given in a set of data.

In locating points in a plane, distances and directions are considered with reference to two guide lines, called *axes*, one drawn vertically and the other drawn horizontally. The vertical reference line is usually called the y *axis*, and the horizontal line is called the x *axis*. Their point of intersection is called the *origin*. The four sections into which these lines divide the plane are called *quadrants* and are numbered I, II, III, IV, as indicated in Fig. 76. Measures of distances toward the right from the y axis are indicated by positive numbers, and measures of distances toward the left are indicated by negative

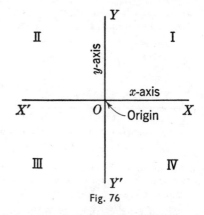

Fig. 76

numbers. Similarly, measures of distances upward from the x axis are considered positive, and measures downward are considered negative.

The position of a point in the plane is definitely determined by a pair of numbers. One number, called the *abscissa*, indicates the distance and direction of the point from the y axis; the other number, called the *ordinate*, indicates the distance and direction of the point from the x axis. Together, the *abscissa* and the *ordinate* are called the *coördinates* of the point. In indicating the coördinates of a point on a graph it is customary to write the numbers representing their values in parentheses near the point, always placing the abscissa first and separating it from the ordinate by a comma. For convenience in measuring distances, each axis may be provided with a scale, or, better still, the drawings may be made on rectangular-coördinate paper (paper that has been cross-ruled into squares).

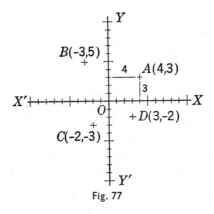

Fig. 77

Example

In Fig. 77 are plotted the points A(4, 3), B(−3, 5), C(−2, −3), and D(3, −2).

Problems

1. Give the coördinates of each of the points, A, B, C, D, E, F, and G in Fig. 78.

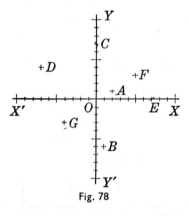

Fig. 78

2. Draw a pair of axes and plot the points $P_1(-5, 2)$, $P_2(4, -3)$, $P_3(5, 2)$, and $P_4(-4, -3)$.

3. Plot the points $(0, 2)$, $(-3, 3)$, $(4\frac{1}{2}, 2)$, $(5, 1\frac{3}{4})$, and $(\frac{11}{3}, 0)$.

4. Draw the line that includes every point whose abscissa is 3.

5. Draw the line that includes every point whose ordinate is $5\frac{1}{2}$.

6. Draw the line that passes through every point whose abscissa and ordinate are equal.

The line graph is well suited for showing a relation between two variable quantities, particularly if the measures of one of the quantities are dependent upon the measures of the other quantity. For example, the yield of wheat per acre depends in part upon the precipitation of moisture (by rain or snow). The relation between these two quantities, as determined approximately for a certain year's crop, is shown in the accompanying table.

This data may be presented graphically by letting each measure of precipitation and the corresponding measure of yield be the abscissa and the ordinate, respectively, of a point, and joining from left to right by a smooth curve the points plotted. The graph obtained is shown in Fig. 79. The scales used are indicated on the two axes. Notice how the ordinates (representing yield) increase as the precipitation increases, up to the point at which the precipitation is 30 in., and then begin to decrease.

Practically all of the coördinate graphs with which the student of

Precipitation (inches)	Yield per Acre (bushels)
10	10
15	14
20	16
25	18
30	19
35	18
40	16
45	$13\frac{1}{2}$
50	$10\frac{1}{2}$
55	7

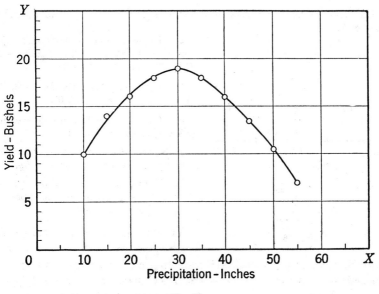

Fig. 79

agriculture will be concerned will lie in the first quadrant, where both the abscissa and the ordinate of every point are positive numbers.

Figure 80 shows several related line graphs and a combination bar and line graph that were made from the data in the table on page 124.

A brief look at the graphs of Fig. 80 reveals that during most periods when the *acreage* planted to potatoes was relatively low the *yield* per acre was usually high, resulting in few extreme variations in total *production*. This indicates that soils of low yield are the first to be withdrawn from plantings as potato production becomes less profitable. Also, it should be observed that *prices* received by farmers for potatoes tend to vary inversely with *production*.

ACREAGE, YIELD, PRODUCTION, AND PRICE OF POTATOES, 1909–1940

Crop Year	Acreage (thousands of Acres)	Yield per Acre (bushels)	Production (thousands of bushels)	Stocks (millions of bushels)	Price per Bushel Received by Farmers
1909	3,675	106.2	390,166		57.6¢
1910	3,644	93.9	342,052		58.4
1911	3,532	85.7	302,713		94.6
1912	3,505	115.9	406,215		56.6
1913	3,477	95.6	332,447		67.8
1914	3,417	107.8	368,249		56.2
1915	3,433	98.1	336,760		67.4
1916	3,274	82.6	270,388		149.7
1917	3,801	104.9	398,653		127.9
1918	3,597	96.2	346,114		118.8
1919	3,300	90.1	297,341	70.0	190.9
1920	3,301	111.8	368,904	112.0	132.8
1921	3,598	90.4	325,312	88.4	112.8
1922	3,901	106.5	415,373	136.7	68.5
1923	3,378	108.5	366,356	109.5	91.4
1924	3,106	123.7	384,166	120.4	71.2
1925	2,810	105.5	296,466	66.3	165.8
1926	2,811	114.4	321,607	80.4	136.1
1927	3,182	116.2	369,644	104.1	108.5
1928	3,499	122.1	427,249	130.0	57.1
1929	3,019	110.0	332,204	82.9	131.8
1930	3,103	109.8	340,572	88.4	91.9
1931	3,467	110.8	384,125	108.2	46.3
1932	3,549	106.1	376,425	109.3	39.2
1933	3,412	100.3	342,306	98.4	82.1
1934	3,597	112.9	406,105	123.7	44.8
1935	3,541	109.1	386,380	106.1	59.7
1936	3,063	108.4	331,918	85.4	114.0
1937	3,185	124.1	395,294	113.2	52.8
1938	3,023	123.8	374,163	103.6	54.8
1939	3,027	120.3	364,016	103.3	68.9
1940*	3,087	124.1	383,172		

* Preliminary.

Potatoes: Acreage, Yield, Production, and Price, United States, 1909 - 40

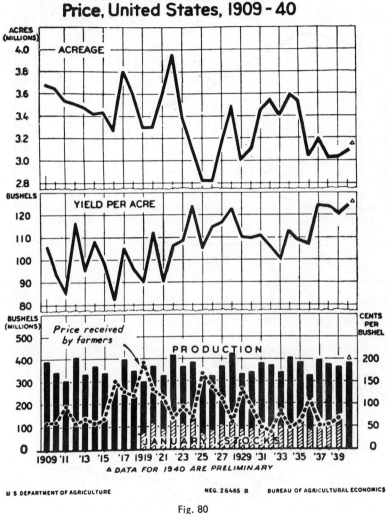

U S DEPARTMENT OF AGRICULTURE   NEG. 26465 B   BUREAU OF AGRICULTURAL ECONOMICS

Fig. 80

The effectiveness of the curve type of graph in presenting quickly time-related trends of subjects is illustrated by Figs. 81 and 82. Little more than a glance at such charts is required for the observer to interpret the data shown.

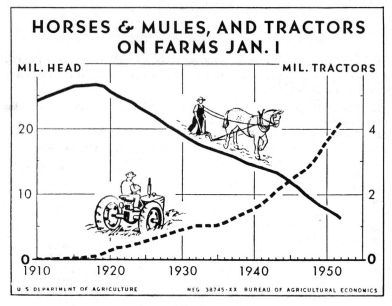

HORSES & MULES, AND TRACTORS ON FARMS JAN. I

MIL. HEAD — MIL. TRACTORS

U S DEPARTMENT OF AGRICULTURE   NEG 38745-XX BUREAU OF AGRICULTURAL ECONOMICS

Fig. 81

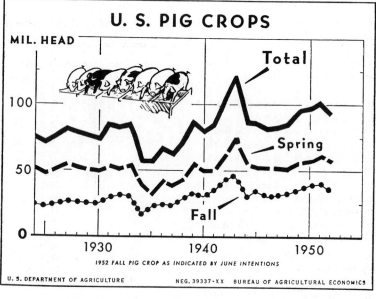

U. S. PIG CROPS

MIL. HEAD

Total

Spring

Fall

1952 FALL PIG CROP AS INDICATED BY JUNE INTENTIONS

U. S. DEPARTMENT OF AGRICULTURE   NEG. 39337-XX   BUREAU OF AGRICULTURAL ECONOMICS

Fig. 82

Problems

1. The capacities of tanks 10 ft in diameter and of various depths are shown in the accompanying table. Prepare a rectangular coördinate graph showing these data.

2. The temperature as read each hour from 6 A.M. to 5 P.M. of a certain winter day was as follows: 6 A.M., −12°; 7 A.M., −10°; 8 A.M., −7°; 9 A.M., −5°; 10 A.M., 0°; 11 A.M., 4°; 12 M., 8°; 1 P.M., 9°; 2 P.M., 10°; 3 P.M., 6°; 4 P.M., 0°; 5 P.M., −6°. Prepare a rectangular coördinate graph showing these data. (*Suggestion:* Represent time along the horizontal axis and temperature ong the vertical axis.)

Depth (*feet*)	Capacity(*barrels*)
8	149.2
9	167.9
10	186.5
11	205.1
12	223.8
13	242.4
14	261.1
15	279.8
16	298.4
17	317.0
18	335.7

3. Determine the interest on $100 at 8% for periods of 1 yr, 2yr, 3 yr, and so on to 10 yr and prepare a rectangular coördinate graph showing the data. From the graph determine the interest on $100 for 4 yr 3 months.

4. The approximate number of tons of corn silage in a silo 12 ft in diameter with silage at various depths is shown in the accompanying table. Prepare a rectangular coördinate graph showing these data.

5. The average price per 100 lb, by months, paid at Chicago in 1939 for beef steers (good grade), was as follows: January, $10.35; February, $10.23; March, $10.64; April, $10.33; May, $9.92; June, $9.29; July, $9.26; August, $9.03; September, $10.20; October, $9.68; November, $9.52; December, $9.44. Prepare a rectangular coördinate graph showing these data.

6. Find the lengths (in rods) of fencing required to inclose square tracts of land containing 1, 2, 3, 4, 5, 10, 15, 20, and 25 acres, respectively, and prepare a rectangular

Depth (*feet*)	Contents (*tons*)
10	19.8
12	24.2
14	28.7
16	33.2
18	37.8
20	42.4
22	47.0
24	51.7
26	56.5
28	61.3
30	66.1
32	70.9
34	75.8
36	80.7
38	85.5
40	90.4

coördinate graph showing the relation between the size of the tract and the length of fencing required.

7. The production of sweet potatoes and the average price per bushel received by farmers in the United States for the years 1925 to 1939 are shown in the accompanying table. Prepare a rectangular coördinate graph showing the production data by one curve and the price data by another.

Year	Production (thousands of bushels)	Price (cents)
1925	50,241	165.1
1926	63,300	117.4
1927	70,897	109.0
1928	59,178	118.0
1929	64,963	117.1
1930	54,415	108.2
1931	66,849	72.7
1932	86,436	54.2
1933	75,248	69.5
1934	77,482	79.8
1935	83,128	70.4
1936	64,144	94.0
1937	75,053	82.5
1938	76,647	73.3
1939	72,679	75.6

8. Compute the capacities (in gallons) of cylindrical tanks 6 ft tall and having diameters of 2, 3, 4, 5, 6, 7, and 8 ft, and make a rectangular coördinate graph showing the relation between the capacity of the tank and the diameter.

9. Determine the quantities of salt that should be added to 100 oz of water to form solutions testing 2, 4, 6, 8, 10, 12, 14, 16, 18, and 20% salt, and prepare a rectangular chart showing these data.

10. Use the following data on the approximate weights of a typical well-bred and well-fed beef steer at different ages to draw a smooth curve showing how the weight of an animal can be expected to increase during the first 30 months of life.

Age (months)	Birth	6	12	18	24	30
Weight (pounds)	80	450	850	1100	1300	1475

11. The numbers of cattle of different weights that may be shipped in a railroad livestock car 36 ft long are:

Average weight (pounds)	300	400	500	600	700	800	900	1000
No. of head	60	50	42	37	33	30	27	25

Draw a curve showing the relation between the average weight of animals shipped and the number constituting a carload.

12. From the following data make a curve graph showing how the velocity of water flowing from a nozzle varies with pressure.

Pressure (lb per sq in.)	10	20	30	40	50	60	70
Velocity (ft per sec)	38.6	54.55	66.85	77.2	86.25	94.5	102.1

13. The relation between the size of the potato crop harvested in the United States and the price received by farmers for certain years is indicated in the following table.

Potatoes	1943	1944	1945	1946	1947	1948	1949
Total harvested (million bu)	458.4	383.4	418.8	484.2	389.0	454.7	402.0
* Price per bushel (dollars)	1.31	1.50	1.43	1.24	1.62	1.55	1.40

* The price has been affected some by the Government surplus removal programs.

Show this relation between production and price by drawing a production curve and a price curve on the same time reference system.

14. Use the following data on domestic uses of wheat in the United States to prepare a chart consisting of line graphs, one for each use, drawn on same reference system.

Domestic Use	1941	1942	1943	1944	1945	1946	1947	1948	1949	1950
Food (million bu)	473.3	500.0	481.9	471.9	473.5	483.3	488.8	479.0	484.1	489.0
Feed (million bu)	114.1	300.8	507.6	302.1	298.5	175.8	183.6	122.1	163.6	150.0
Seed (million bu)	62.5	65.5	77.4	80.4	82.0	86.5	90.7	94.6	81.4	84.0
Industrial (million bu)	1.6	54.4	107.5	82.3	21.0	*	0.6	0.1	0.1	*

* Insignificant quantities.

15. From data of Problem 14 make a chart of bar graphs showing the domestic uses of wheat for each of the years 1941, 1943, 1945.

16. The lengths of common nails of certain sizes and the approximate number of each kind per pound are:

Size of Nail	2d	3d	4d	6d	8d	10d	12d	16d	20d	40d	60d
Length (in.).....	1	1¼	1½	2	2½	3	3¼	3½	4	5	6
Number per pound	830	528	316	168	106	69	63	49	31	18	11

On a single chart display lengths of nails of the various sizes with bar graphs and the relation between size of nail and number per pound with a line graph.

17. The hourly equivalents of all types of farm wage rates and the purchasing value of each rate for certain years from 1910 to 1950 are given in the following table:

	1910	1915	1920	1925	1930	1935	1940	1945	1950
Prevailing rate (cents per hour)..	12.9	13.7	32.2	23.4	22.2	13.7	16.8	46.6	55.3
Purchasing value (cents)	16.1	15.9	17.9	17.6	18.2	13.6	17.1	31.1	26.6

Use the data to plot curves on same reference systems showing the variation of these two quantities during the period of time indicated.

18. Use the following data on the urban and rural population of the United States at 10-year intervals from 1850 to 1949 to draw two curves showing these population increases and obtain from these two curves a third curve showing the total population increase.

	1850	1860	1870	1880	1890	1900	1910	1920	1930	1940	1949
Urban pop. (millions)	3.5	6.2	9.9	14.1	22.1	30.2	42.0	54.1	69.0	74.5	87.4
Rural pop. (millions)	19.7	25.2	28.7	36.0	40.8	45.8	50.0	51.6	53.8	57.2	61.2

19. The average net yearly income for workers engaged in agriculture and for industrial workers for the period from 1910 to 1949 is given at 5-year intervals in the following table. Draw suitable curves exhibiting these data.

Average Net Annual Income	1910	1915	1920	1925	1930	1935	1940	1945	1949
Agr. worker (dollars)	371	381	753	642	489	469	524	1534	1735
Indus. worker (dollars)	605	656	1488	1365	1318	1118	1341	2323	2900

20. For each of certain years listed in the following table the average of prices paid for certain representative commodities is expressed as a per cent of the average of the prices paid during the 5-year base period 1910–1914. The average of prices received by farmers for certain representative products for each of these years is also expressed as a per cent of the average of prices received during the base period.

Average Price	Base 1910–1914	1915	1920	1925	1930	1935	1940	1945	1949
Paid(%)	100	105	214	164	151	124	124	189	250
Received(%)	100	99	212	156	125	109	100	206	249

Exhibit these facts graphically by drawing two suitable curves on the same reference system, and a straight horizontal line at the 100% level to represent the reference base.

21. On the same reference system draw two curves, one showing the annual production of hogs and the other showing the average price per 100 lb of live weight received by farmers for hogs in the United States for certain years, as indicated in the following table.

Hogs	1925	1930	1935	1940	1945	1949
Number produced (thousands)	70,310	74,135	56,144	79,866	86,782	199,079
Price per 100 lb (dollars)	10.91	8.84	8.65	5.39	14.00	18.10

22. Use the following data to obtain three curves on the same reference system, one showing the total number of milk cows in the United States for certain years, another showing the total annual production of whole milk produced and a third curve showing the annual production per cow. (It is suggested that different vertical scales be used for the three items.)

	1925	1930	1935	1940	1945	1950*
Milk cows (thousands) ...	21,503	22,218	24,187	23,677	25,329	22,740
Total production (million pounds)	90,699	100,158	101,205	109,502	121,504	122,000
Production per cow (pounds).............	4,218	4,508	4,184	4,625	4,797	5,365

* Preliminary estimate.

23. Show by suitable curves on a single reference system the variations of the annual consumptions of butter and margarine per person in the United States according to the following data.

Consumption per Person	1915	1920	1925	1930	1935	1940	1945	1950*
Butter (pounds)	17.1	14.7	17.9	17.2	17.1	16.9	10.9	10.2
Margarine (pounds).....	1.4	3.4	2.0	2.6	3.0	2.4	4.0	6.1

* Preliminary estimate.

24. Draw curves on the same reference system to compare variations in prices of butter and margarine in accordance with the following data.

Retail Price per Pound of	1920	1925	1930	1935	1940	1945	1950
Butter (cents) ..	70.1	55.2	46.4	36.0	36.0	50.7	72.3
Margarine (cents)	42.3	30.2	25.0	18.8	15.9	24.1	28.8

25. Prepare a two-curve chart showing the average number of laying hens in the United States and the total annual egg production for the years shown in the following:

	1925	1930	1935	1940	1945	1950*
Layers (thousands)......	311,342	321,893	276,406	296,596	369,363	356,000
Egg production (millions)	34,969	39,067	33,609	39,695	55,858	59,580

* Preliminary estimate.

26. Use the following data to obtain a curve showing the rise in the average annual production of eggs per hen during the period 1925–1950.

	1925	1926	1927	1928	1929	1930	1931	1932	1933	1934
Eggs per hen	112	118	117	119	119	121	127	121	118	118

	1935	1936	1937	1938	1939	1940	1941	1942	1943	1944
Eggs per hen	122	121	130	135	134	134	139	142	142	148

	1945	1946	1947	1948	1949	1950
Eggs per hen	151	155	158	162	165	167

Graph of an Equation

In many cases the relation between two quantities may be expressed by an equation which involves letters that represent the measures of the quantities considered. By assigning numerical values to one of the letters and finding corresponding values of the other, a table of data can be set up from which a rectangular coördinate graph may be drawn. If the graph so obtained contains all points, and only those points, whose coördinates satisfy the given equation, it is called the *graph of the equation*.

As an example we may consider the relation between distance and time in the case of a body moving at a constant rate. Suppose that an automobile is traveling at the rate of 1 mi. per minute. Then if y stands for the number of miles traveled in x min., we have the relation $y = x$.

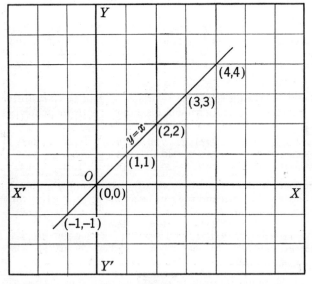

Fig. 83

Obviously the graph of this equation consists of every point whose y-coördinate is the same as its x-coördinate. The coördinates of a few such points are given in the accompanying table, and these points are plotted on the graph in Fig. 83. Many other pairs of numbers could be found that would serve as the coördinates of points on the graph.

x	y
-1	-1
0	0
1	1
3	3
4	4

Next consider the relation between x and y that is expressed by the equation $x + y = 5$. To obtain a point on the graph of this equation one needs merely to find a pair of numbers, one a value of x and the other the corresponding value

x	y
−1	6
0	5
1	4
2	3
3	2
3½	1½
5	0

of y, whose sum is 5. A brief table of values is shown at the left. The points represented by these pairs of numbers are plotted in Fig. 84.

In making a table of values for the graph of an equation, it is usually convenient to solve the equation for one letter in terms of the other. For example, suppose the equation

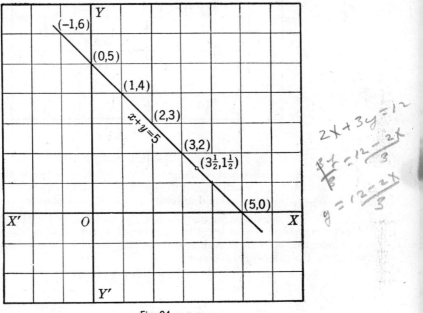

Fig. 84

under consideration is

$$2x + 3y = 12.$$

Solving this equation for y, we obtain

$$y = \frac{12 - 2x}{3}.$$

x	y
−2	$\frac{16}{3}$
0	4
1	$\frac{10}{3}$
2	$\frac{8}{3}$
3	2
6	0
7	$-\frac{2}{3}$

Now we may proceed to assign values to x and find corresponding values of y, thus forming a table of paired numbers like the one at the right. The points represented by these pairs of numbers are plotted on the graph in Fig. 85.

A complete treatment of the subject of equations and their graphs,

which is one of the main topics in the field of analytic geometry, is beyond
the scope of this book.

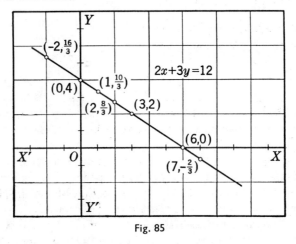

Fig. 85

Problems

1. Write an equation indicating the relation between the interest
on $100 at 6% per annum and the number of years this sum is at interest.
Make a table of values and draw the graph of the equation.

2. If r stands for the number of linear units in the length of the radius
of a circle and A stands for the number of square units in the area of the
circle, the relation between A and r is expressed by the equation $A = \pi r^2$.
Draw the graph of this equation.

Draw the graph of each of the following equations:

3. $y = 3x$.

4. $y = 3x + 2$. Compare this graph with that of the preceding
problem.

5. $3y = 2x$.

6. $6y = 4x$. Compare this graph with that of the preceding problem.
Note that the two equations express the same relation between x and y.

7. $3x - 2y = 6$.

8. $y = x^2$.

9. $y = x^2 - 2x - 15$.

10. $y = x^3$.

11. The number of dollars, y, that a certain firm pays for 100 lb
of milk testing x% butterfat is given by the following formula:
$y = 7.56 + 0.07(x - 4)$. Using whole number values of x ranging from
2 to 6, draw the graph of this equation.

12. From the graph made in Problem 11, determine the price per hundredweight to be paid for milk having each of the following per cent butterfat ratings: 2.8, 3.6, 4.3, 4.9, 5.4.

Graph of a System of Equations

In our study of the system of equations

$$\begin{cases} x + y = 5. \\ x - y = 1. \end{cases}$$

in Chapter 3 it was pointed out that each of these equations, considered separately, has infinitely many solutions. Since each solution of such an equation consists of a pair of numbers that designate a point on the graph of the equation, we may say that the graph of each of these equations is made up of the infinitely many points determined by the infinitely many solutions. In Fig. 84 a portion of the graph of the equation $x + y = 5$ is shown. If the graph of the equation $x - y = 1$ be plotted on the same set of axes it will be observed that the two graphs (which, in this case, are straight lines) intersect at the point (3,2). This might reasonably be expected from the fact that $x = 3$ and $y = 2$ constitute a *solution* of the system of equations, thus insuring that the point (3,2) should be on both graphs. The following significant fact is thus illustrated: *The coördinates of a point of intersection of the graphs of two equations in x and y constitute a solution of the system of equations.*

Problems

Draw the graphs of the two equations of each of the following systems on the same set of axes and determine (at least, approximately) the solution (or solutions) of each system. Test out the results so obtained by actual substitution in the equations or by solving each system algebraically.

1. $\begin{cases} x + y = 5. \\ x - y = 1. \end{cases}$

2. $\begin{cases} y = x. \\ x + 2y = 6. \end{cases}$

3. $\begin{cases} 2x - 3y = 12. \\ 3x + y = 7. \end{cases}$

4. $\begin{cases} 2y - 3x = 12. \\ x + y = -4. \end{cases}$

5. $\begin{cases} y = x^2. \\ x - y + 2 = 0. \end{cases}$

6. $\begin{cases} x + 2y = 4. \\ 2x + 4y = 10. \end{cases}$

Do the graphs of these equations appear to intersect? Are the equations consistent or do they express relations that are contradictory? Does the system have a solution?

7. $\begin{cases} y = 6x - x^2. \\ y = 2x. \end{cases}$

8. $\begin{cases} x^2 + y^2 = 25. \\ x - 2y + 5 = 0. \end{cases}$

CHAPTER 9

SPECIAL APPLICATIONS OF PRACTICAL MEASUREMENTS

Concrete Making

Concrete is made by mixing cement, sand, and gravel in various proportions with enough water to give the mixture a workable consistency. The proportion in which the dry ingredients are mixed depends upon the use to be made of the finished concrete. By a 1–2–4 mixture is meant a mixture consisting by volume of 1 part of cement, 2 parts of sand, and 4 parts of gravel. In high-grade concrete the sand with its voids or air spaces fills the voids in the gravel, and the cement fills the remaining voids, so that the volume of the resulting mixture is much less than the total volume of the ingredients used. In computing the materials needed for concrete work either of two methods may be used with satisfactory results.

Methods of Computing Volumes of Materials Needed

Method I. This method is based upon the fact that about 42 cu ft of unmixed cement, sand, and gravel are required to make 1 cu yd (27 cu ft) of concrete. Since $42 \div 27 = 1\frac{5}{9}$, the sum of the volumes of unmixed materials required is about $1\frac{5}{9}$ times the volume of concrete to be made.

Example

How many cubic feet each of cement, sand, and gravel are required to make 240 cu ft of a 1-2-4 mixture of concrete?

$1\frac{5}{9} \times 240 = 373\frac{1}{3}$, the number of cubic feet of unmixed materials required.

In a 1-2-4 mixture the volume of cement is one-seventh of the total volume of materials.

$\frac{1}{7} \times 373\frac{1}{3} = 53\frac{1}{3}$, the number of cubic feet of cement.
$2 \times 53\frac{1}{3} = 106\frac{2}{3}$, the number of cubic feet of sand.
$4 \times 53\frac{1}{3} = 213\frac{1}{3}$, the number of cubic feet of gravel.

In practice, one might assume that 53 cu ft of cement, 107 cu ft of sand, and 213 cu ft of gravel are required.

Method II.   Voids are usually considered as making up 45% of a volume of gravel or crushed stone and $33\frac{1}{3}\%$ of a volume of sand.   Therefore about 55% of the volume of gravel used, $66\frac{2}{3}\%$ of the volume of sand used, and all of the cement used actually go toward making the volume of finished concrete.   The per cents of void spaces in the sand and gravel can be used as a basis for computing the quantities of materials needed to produce a certain quantity of concrete, as indicated in the following example.

Example

Using the per cents of void spaces mentioned above, determine the number of cubic feet each of cement, sand, and gravel required to make 240 cu ft of a 1-2-4 mixture of concrete.

Let C = the number of cubic feet of cement required,

S = the number of cubic feet of sand required,

and G = the number of cubic feet of gravel required.

Then, since all of the volume of the cement, $66\frac{2}{3}\%$ of the volume of the sand, and 55% of the volume of the gravel together make up the required volume of concrete, we have

$$C + 0.667S + 0.55G = 240.$$

Since a 1-2-4 mixture is to be used, it follows that

$$S = 2C$$

and $$G = 4C.$$

The system of equations

$$\begin{cases} (1) & C + 0.667S + 0.55G = 240 \\ (2) & S = 2C \\ (3) & G = 4C \end{cases}$$

is readily solved by using Equations (2) and (3) to substitute for S and G in Equation (1).

$$C + 0.667(2C) + 0.55(4C) = 240.$$
$$C + 1.334C + 2.20C = 240.$$
$$4.5C = 240, \text{ approximately.}$$
$$C = 53.3, \text{ approximately.}$$
$$S = 2(53.3) = 106.6, \text{ approximately.}$$
$$G = 4(53.3) = 213.2, \text{ approximately.}$$

Thus, in a 1-2-4 mixture about 53 cu ft of cement, 107 cu ft of sand, and 213 cu ft of gravel are required to make 240 cu ft of concrete.   Note that these results are consistent with those obtained by Method I.

Other methods. Several other methods of estimating the quantities of materials required in concrete making are used to some extent.

One method, often referred to as "the 10% method" or as "the 90% method," is based upon the assumption that the volume of gravel required is about 90% of the volume of concrete to be made. In practice, the volume of gravel required is often arrived at by subtracting from the volume of concrete 10% of itself. Estimates are easily formed on this basis but are not considered as reliable as those obtained by Methods I and II.

Applying this method to the problem previously solved by Methods I and II, we obtain

$$10\% \text{ of } 240 = 24,$$

$$240 - 24 = 216, \text{ number of cubic feet of gravel,}$$

$$\tfrac{1}{4} \text{ of } 216 = 54, \text{ number of cubic feet of cement,}$$

and

$$2(54) = 108, \text{ number of cubic feet of sand.}$$

As a basis for making quickly a rough estimate of the quantities of materials needed, one may assume that the total volume of unmixed materials required is about $1\tfrac{1}{2}$ times the volume of concrete to be made. Using this assumption on the problem previously considered, we have

$$1\tfrac{1}{2} \times 240 = 360, \text{ number of cubic feet of materials,}$$

$$360 \div 7 = 51, \text{ number of cubic feet of cement,}$$

$$51 \times 2 = 102, \text{ number of cubic feet of sand,}$$

and

$$51 \times 4 = 204, \text{ number of cubic feet of gravel.}$$

The student may find this procedure of value in, checking results obtained by the more reliable methods. He can at least tell in this way whether or not the results obtained are reasonable.

Formulas for Computing Volumes of Materials Needed

The assumption that 42 cu ft of unmixed materials are required to make 1 cu yd of concrete is used as the basis for the following formulas, which the student may readily verify. If C, S, and G denote the numbers of cubic feet of cement, sand, and gravel, respectively, required to make 1 *cu yd of concrete* in which the proportional parts of cement, sand, and gravel are indicated (by *small case* letters) in the formula $c-s-g$, then

$$C = \frac{42c}{c + s + g},$$

$$S = \frac{42s}{c + s + g},$$

and

$$G = \frac{42g}{c + s + g}.$$

Usually, c is taken as 1 in a ratio formula; however, it is sometimes convenient to replace a $1-2\frac{1}{2}-4$ formula, for example, by the equivalent $2-5-8$ formula.

Proportions of cement, sand, and gravel commonly used in concrete work are given in Table IV, page 185.

Problems

By Method I find the amount of materials needed per cubic yard of the following concrete mixtures:

1. A 1-2-5 mixture.
2. A 1-1-2 mixture.
3. A 1-1½-3 mixture.
4. A 1-3-6 mixture. — *Both Methods*
5. A 1-2½-5 mixture.

6-10. Solve Problems 1–5 by use of Method II, using the per cents of void spaces in sand and gravel mentioned above.

11. Compute the quantity of materials needed in making 200 cu ft of a 1-2-3 concrete.

12. How much cement, sand, and gravel are needed to construct a concrete walk 4 ft wide, 30 ft long, and 6 in. thick if a 1-2-5 mixture is used?

13. What quantities of ingredients are required for making 40 cylindrical concrete pillars 20 in. in diameter and 30 in. long if a 1-2-4 mixture is used?

14. How much cement, sand, and gravel are needed to make 25 concrete piers each 2 ft long and each having a lower base 2 ft square and an upper base 1 ft square if a 1-2-4 mixture is used?

15. What amounts of materials are needed in constructing a wall 1 ft thick for a cylindrical concrete silo 40 ft high with an inside diameter of 12 ft if the mixture is 1-2½-4?

16. How much cement, sand, and gravel are required to construct a concrete floor 40 ft long, 30 ft wide, and 6 in. thick if a 1-3-5 mixture is used?

17. How many cubic feet each of cement, sand, and gravel are required in making 35 concrete cylindrical pillars 2 ft in diameter and 30 in. long if a 1-2½-5 mixture is used?

18. A concrete watering trough 6 ft long, 3 ft wide, and 2 ft deep (outside measurements) with walls and bottom 6 in. thick is made from a 1-2-3 mixture. If the sand and gravel are bought already mixed at $4 per cubic yard and the cement is bought at 90¢ per cubic foot, what is the total cost of cement, sand, and gravel used in making the trough?

19. Calculate the raw materials needed in a 1-2½-3 mixture to build a sidewalk 4 ft wide, 90 ft long, and 5 in. thick. If cement is $1.10 a sack and sand and gravel are $4.25 a cubic yard, what would be the cost of these materials?

20. A concrete foundation for a house 24 ft by 36 ft (outside measurements) is to be 12 in. wide at the bottom, 8 in. wide at the top, and 28 in. deep. How many cubic feet each of cement, sand, and gravel are needed if a 1-2-4 mixture is used?

21. How many cubic feet of cement, sand containing 30% voids, and gravel containing 50% voids must be used in a 1-2-4 mixture to make 1000 cu ft of concrete?

22. How much cement, sand containing 35% voids, and gravel containing 40% voids are needed in a 1-2½-5 mixture to make 1000 cu ft of concrete?

Measurement of Lumber

The measure of lumber is expressed in board feet (bd ft), 1 bd ft being defined as the measure of a piece of lumber 1 ft square and 1 in. thick. The number of board feet in a piece of lumber is given by the formula

$$\text{Bd ft} = \frac{\text{Thickness in inches} \times \text{width in inches} \times \text{length in feet}}{12},$$

where the symbol " $\times$ " is read as "by" and where thicknesses of less than 1 in. are counted as 1 in. and other thicknesses are counted as they are given in the description of the piece of lumber.

Problems

Find the number of board feet in each of the following:

1. 32 planks 3″ × 8″ × 16′.

2. 50 pieces 2″ × 4″ × 12′.

3. 12 pieces 4″ × 6″ × 14′.

4. 200 pieces ½″ × 1½″ × 16′.

5. 150 pieces ¾″ × 4″ × 24′.

6. At $40 per M (1000 bd ft), how much should the siding (1 in. thick) for a barn 28 ft by 56 ft cost if the wall is 10 ft high and no allowance is made for openings?

7. About how many board feet of sheathing 1 in. by 4 in. are required for a gable roof of a barn if each side of the roof measures 18 by 40 ft and the laths are placed 4 in. apart?

8. Allowing for 3 pickets ¾ in. by 2 in. by 4 ft for each linear foot of fence, find the number of board feet of lumber in a 100-ft roll of pickets.

9. The walls, gables, and roof sheathing of a garage 20 ft long and 18 ft wide with walls 8 ft high are made of lumber 1 in. thick. The roof has a pitch of ½, and there is no overhang. Find the number of board feet of this kind of lumber required, making no allowance for openings.

10. The floor of a building measures 28 ft by 60 ft. The sills measure 4 in. by 6 in. in cross section and extend along the sides and ends and lengthwise through the center; the floor joists measure 2 in. by 8 in. by 14 ft, rest on the sills, crosswise to the building, and are 2 ft apart from center to center. Find the number of board feet of lumber in the sills and floor joists of this building.

11. The wall of a cylindrical silo 14 ft in outside diameter and 35 ft high is constructed of wooden staves 2 in. thick. Determine approximately the number of board feet of lumber contained in the wall of this silo.

12. From frequent practice in computing board measure, lumbermen associate with the various descriptions of cross sections of lumber certain numbers that may be applied directly to total lengths to give board measure. The number applied in a particular case is one-twelfth of the number of square inches in the cross-sectional area of a piece of the lumber. For example, the number of board feet in a lot of 2 in. by 4 in. pieces of lumber is simply (2 × 4)/12, or ⅔, times the total number of linear feet of the lumber. Complete the table at the right, in which the board measure of certain sizes of lumber is expressed in terms of the length.

Description of Cross Section (inches)	Board Feet in Terms of Length
1 × 2	....
1 × 4	⅓ of length
1 × 6	....
1 × 8	....
1 × 12	....
2 × 4	....
2 × 6	....
2 × 8	....
2 × 12	....
4 × 4	....
4 × 6	....
6 × 6	....
6 × 8	....
8 × 10	....
8 × 12	....

Measuring Lumber in the Log

For practical purposes the number of board feet of lumber that may be obtained from a log of certain size is given with fair accuracy by the following rule, which is known as *Doyle's rule*: *From the number of inches in the smallest diameter of the log subtract 4, multiply the remainder by half itself, multiply this result by the number of feet in the length of the log, and divide by 8.*

For example, the number of board feet in a log 16 ft long and having a smallest diameter of 18 in. is approximately

$$\frac{(18 - 4) \times 7 \times 16}{8} = \frac{14 \times 7 \times 16}{8} = 196.$$

Another formulation of the above rule is

$$\text{Bd ft} = \frac{(\text{least diameter in inches} - 4)^2 \times \text{length in feet}}{16}.$$

Problems

Determine approximately the number of board feet of lumber in logs with the following dimensions:

1. Length, 24 ft; smallest diameter, 12 in.
2. Length, 20 ft; smallest diameter, 14 in.
3. Length, 28 ft; smallest diameter, 30 in.
4. Length, 16 ft; smallest diameter, 24 in.
5. Length, 18 ft; smallest diameter, 18 in.

Measuring Lumber in the Tree

Table V, page 185, gives approximately the number of board feet of lumber in trees of various diameters and consisting of one, two, or three 16-ft logs.

Measuring Hay in Stacks

In all problems thus far considered involving the measurement of hay in stacks we have assumed the stack of hay in each case to be in the form of some geometric solid whose volume could be readily computed. The student realizes that most haystacks are not of such ideal shape. Then how may the content of a haystack be measured satisfactorily?

As a result of a study made by the United States Department of Agriculture in coöperation with a number of state agricultural experimental stations, in which several thousand oblong and round stacks were measured in the Western and Great Plain states, the following methods for volume measurement were developed.*

---

* Leaflet No. 72, United States Department of Agriculture.

Oblong Stacks

All oblong stacks are divided into three types, as indicated in Fig. 86. The volume (denoted by V) in each case is computed from three measurements: the width of the stack at the ground (denoted by W), the average length of the stack (denoted by L), and the "over" (denoted by T), which

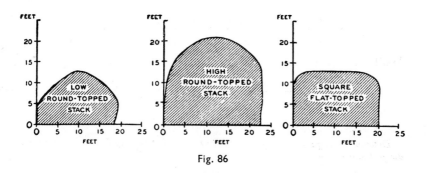

Fig. 86

is the distance from the ground on one side over the stack to the ground on the other side. The formulas for making the computations are as follows:

For low round-topped stacks,

$$V = (0.52T - 0.44W)WL;$$

for high round-topped stacks,

$$V = (0.52T - 0.46W)WL;$$

and for square flat-topped stacks,

$$V = (0.56T - 0.55W)WL.$$

Example

Find the number of cubic feet of hay in a high round-topped stack 20 ft wide, 45 ft over, and 50 ft long.

$$V = [0.52(45) - 0.46(20)] (20) (50)$$
$$= [23.40 - 9.20] (1000)$$
$$= [14.20] (1000)$$
$$= 14,200.$$

The stack contains approximately 14,200 cu ft.

Round Stacks

A fairly satisfactory formula for the volume, V, of a round stack is given in terms of the circumference, C, of the base and the over, T, taken over the highest point:

$$V = (0.04T - 0.012C)(C^2).$$

Example

Determine the volume of a round stack 100 ft in circumference and having an over of 60 ft.

$$V = (0.04 \times 60 - 0.012 \times 100) (100)^2$$
$$= 12,000.$$

The volume is approximately 12,000 cu ft.

In actual practice the diagrams of Fig. 86 may be helpful in classifying a haystack to determine which formula should be applied.

Problems

Find approximately the volume of each of the stacks of hay described below.

1. Low round-topped, 18 ft wide, 35 ft over, 40 ft long.
2. Square flat-topped, 20 ft wide, 45 ft over, 50 ft long.
3. High round-topped, 25 ft wide, 55 ft over, 56 ft long.
4. Round, 80 ft in circumference, 45 ft over.
5. Round, 100 ft in circumference, 60 ft over.

Measurements Relating to Silos

After feeding from a silo has begun it is usually desirable to remove at regular intervals a cross-sectional slice of silage of certain minimum thickness to prevent spoilage. The required thickness of the slice depends mainly upon the kind of silage and prevailing climatic conditions. To insure removal of a slice of sufficient thickness, the maximum cross-sectional area of a silo should be determined by the least quantity of silage to be fed daily over any portion of the feeding period.

Example

What should be the dimensions of a cylindrical silo of maximum cross-sectional area which is to provide each of 30 cows with 40 lb of silage daily for 140 days if it is desirable to remove a slice of silage 3 in. thick each day to prevent spoilage?

First, the diameter of the silo should be determined.

Let r = the number of feet in the radius of the silo.

1 cu ft of silage weighs about 40 lb. Then the slice to be fed daily contains about 30 cu ft.

$$3 \text{ in.} = \tfrac{1}{4} \text{ ft.}$$

Then $$\pi r^2(\tfrac{1}{4}) = 30.$$

$$\pi r^2 = 120.$$

$$r^2 = \frac{120}{\pi} = 38.2, \text{ approximately.}$$

$$r = 6.2, \text{ approximately.}$$

The silo should be about 12.4 ft in inside diameter.

The number of feet in the height of the silo is simply the number of days in the feeding period times the number of feet in the thickness of the slice to be removed each day. Thus,

$$140 \times \tfrac{1}{4} = 35.$$

The silo should be about 35 ft high.

Problems

1. A certain cylindrical silo is 40 ft high and 14 ft in inside diameter. (a) If 1 cu ft of silage weighs 40 lb, how many tons of silage can be stored in this silo? (b) How many pounds of silage would be contained in a cross-sectional slice 3 in. thick? (c) Such a slice would provide how many cows with 40 lb of silage each? (d) If a 3-in. slice is fed daily, the silo provides for a feeding period of what length?

2. What should be the dimensions of a cylindrical silo for a herd of 36 cows if a ration of 40 lb is fed daily for 120 days and it is desirable to remove a 4-in. slice of silage each day?

3. A silo is 16 ft in inside diameter and 36 ft high. If it is desirable to feed a 3-in. slice daily, this silo will provide a daily ration of 30 lb per head for how many cows? For what length of feeding period does the silo provide?

4. What should be the dimensions of a cylindrical silo to provide 30 cows with 40 lb each daily for 100 days, 30 lb each for 50 days, and 20 lb each for 30 days, if the minimum thickness of slice to be removed daily over any portion of the feeding period is 2.5 in.? (If a given set of requirements indicate that the height of a silo should be greater than 50 ft, it is usually considered best to build two silos of suitable heights, having together the required capacity, instead of one.)

5. A rule often followed in determining the proper cross-sectional area of a silo is the allowance of a cross-sectional feeding surface of 5 sq ft for each cow to be fed. If the daily ration is 1 cu ft of silage per head, application of the above rule would result in removal of a slice of silage of what thickness each day?

6. The cross section of a certain silo is a hexagon (a plane figure with six sides) each side of which is 6 ft long (inside measurement). Determine the cross-sectional area of the silo and from that the minimum number of cattle that should be fed 1 cu ft each per day to insure a feeding depth of 2 in. per day. If this silo is 35 ft high, about how many tons of silage does it hold when it is full?

7. The wall of a certain silo consists of 12 sides each 4 ft wide (inside measurement). If the silo is 40 ft high, about how many tons of silage will it hold when full?

8. A certain trench silo having a trapezoidal cross section measuring 7 ft across the bottom, 11 ft across the top, and 8 ft in depth, is 50 ft long. If it is desirable in feeding to remove a slice 4 in. thick crosswise to the trench each day, what is the minimum number of cattle that should be fed 1 cu ft of silage each per day? On this basis, for what length of feeding period does the silo provide? What is the capacity of the silo in tons if 1 cu ft weighs 30 lb?

9. A trench silo is to be constructed so as to provide 1 cu ft of silage per head daily for a herd of 25 cattle. If a slice 4 in. thick is to be fed daily, what should be the cross-sectional area of the trench? Work out a set of dimensions for the silo, making it 10 ft deep and long enough to provide for a 90-day feeding period.

Feeds

It is not intended that the treatment of feeds given here be considered authoritative or complete. The aim is simply to familiarize the student with certain calculations applicable to problems that arise in a study of feeds.

As previously stated, the main constituents of feeds are (1) proteins, (2) ether extract (fats and oils), (3) nitrogen-free extract (chiefly carbohydrates, such as sugars and starches), (4) crude fiber (cell walls and woody materials of plants), (5) ash (residue obtained from burning a feed), and (6) water. The first four of these are usually spoken of as the nutrients of a feed. Table VIII, page 188, gives the average percentage composition of certain feeding stuffs. The digestibility of feed nutrients varies with different feeds containing them and with different animals consuming them. However, from numerous feeding experiments average figures, called *coefficients of digestibility*, have been obtained which indicate for a particular feed the per cents of the nutrients that are digestible. The numbers of pounds of digestible nutrients per 100 lb of certain feeds, as indicated in Table IX, page 189, were obtained by applying such a set of digestibility coefficients to the weights of the nutrients in 100 lb shown in Table VIII.

Table IX also gives for each feed listed the number of therms of productive energy furnished by 100 lb of the feed. A therm is the amount of heat or energy required to raise the temperature of 1000 kg of water 1°C. While figures on productive energy are usually obtained from experimental measurement of the fat-producing quality of feeds, they may be considered as indicative of the value of feeds for animal maintenance and for production of flesh, animal products such as milk and eggs, and energy to be used in performing work.

A factor usually considered significant in determining whether or not a feed or feed mixture constitutes a balanced ration for an animal is the *nutritive ratio* of the ration. The nutritive ratio of a feed or ration is the ratio of the weight of digestible protein to the weight of digestible carbohydrate equivalents furnished by the nonprotein nutrients contained in the feed or ration. The weight of digestible carbohydrate equivalents is the sum of the weights of digestible nitrogen-free extract, digestible crude fiber, and 2.25 times the weight of digestible ether extract. The weight of digestible ether extract (mainly fats) is multiplied by 2.25 for the reason that as a source of energy 1 lb of fat is equivalent to about 2.25 lb of carbohydrate. In expressing a nutritive ratio the first term (or numerator) of the ratio is taken as 1, and the second term (or denominator) is computed by combining the weight of digestible nitrogen-free extract and digestible crude fiber with 2.25 times the weight of digestible ether extract and dividing this sum by the weight of digestible crude protein. Since the totals of digestible nutrients given in Table IX include 2.25 times the digestible fats, the second term of the ratio for a feed may be obtained by subtracting the weight of digestible protein from the total weight of digestible nutrients and dividing this difference by the weight of digestible protein. Thus, if R denotes the nutritive ratio, T denotes the total weight of digestible nutrients, and P denotes the weight of digestible protein, we have

$$R = \frac{1}{(T - P) \div P}$$

In balanced rations for different types of livestock, nutritive ratios usually vary within the following ranges:

Beef cattle...............................1 : 4 to 1 : 9
Dairy cattle..............................1 : 3 to 1 : 7
Hogs.....................................1 : 4 to 1 : 7
Horses ....1 : 6 to 1 : 9
Poultry ....1 : 3 to 1 : 8
Sheep....................................1 : 5 to 1 : 9

Various standards of feeding requirements for different types of livestock have been derived from feeding experiments.   It is not within the scope of this book to discuss the merits of these standards or to examine the bases upon which they are founded.   Table X, page 190, gives a set of standards based upon animal requirements of (1) productive energy, (2) digestible crude protein, and (3) bulk of dry matter in ration.

Costs of feeds may be compared on the basis of content of one or more of the following: digestible protein, total digestible nutrients, productive energy.

Examples

1.   Determine the nutritive ratio of a horse and mule feed consisting of 50 lb of corn, 35 lb of oats, 14 lb of wheat bran, and 1 lb of salt.

	Digestible Protein	Total Digestible Nutrients
Corn	$50 \times 0.064 = 3.200$	$50 \times 0.823 = 41.150$
Oats	$35 \times 0.096 = 3.360$	$35 \times 0.814 = 28.490$
Wheat bran ..	$14 \times 0.133 = 1.862$	$14 \times 0.617 = 8.638$
Total	8.422	78.278

Digestible non-protein $= 78.278 - 8.422 = 69.856$

$69.856 \div 8.42 = 8.3$ approximately.

Hence, 1 : 8.3 is the nutritive ratio of this feed mixture.

2.   Compute the number of therms of productive energy furnished by 10 lb of hog feed consisting of 6 lb of corn meal, 1.5 lb of ground oats, 1.5 lb of wheat gray shorts, 0.5 lb of tankage, and 0.5 lb of cottonseed meal.

$0.06 \times 86.8 = 5.2080$, number of therms furnished by corn meal.
$0.015 \times 71.9 = 1.0785$, number of therms furnished by oats.
$0.015 \times 75.7 = 1.1355$, number of therms furnished by shorts.
$0.005 \times 59.7 = 0.2985$, number of therms furnished by tankage.
$0.005 \times 74.9 = 0.3745$, number of therms furnished by cottonseed meal.

8.0950, or 8.1, approximate number of therms of productive energy supplied by 10 lb of this feed.

3.   Determine the number of pounds each of corn, cottonseed meal, and cottonseed hulls needed to form a ration whose bulk is about 24 lb and which is to supply 1.6 lb of digestible protein and 13 therms of productive energy.

It is assumed that the 24 lb of bulk includes the normal amount of water contained in the several feeds and that reduction to a basis of dry matter content is not necessary in this case.

The method used here may be described as that of successive trial replacements.

First, suppose that the roughage, cottonseed hulls, makes up the total bulk of 24 lb. The quantity of hulls provides $24 \times 0.179 = 4.296$ therms of productive energy.

Suppose now that some of the hulls are replaced (pound for pound) by sufficient corn to increase the productive energy from 4.296 to the required 13 therms. For each pound of hulls replaced by a pound of corn a gain of $0.848 - 0.179 = 0.669$ therms occurs. Hence $(13 - 4.296) \div 0.669 = 8.704 \div 0.669 = 13$ is the number of pounds of corn to be used in this first replacement.

The number of pounds of digestible protein called for in the ration is now compared with that contained in the 11 lb of hulls and 13 lb of corn. These quantities of hulls and corn contain $11 \times 0.004 + 13 \times 0.064 = 0.044 + 0.832 = 0.876$ lb of digestible protein. Cottonseed meal, which is high in protein, may now replace some of the corn in sufficient quantity to raise the protein content from 0.876 lb to the desired 1.6 lb. For each pound of corn replaced by a pound of cottonseed meal a gain of $0.359 - 0.064 = 0.295$ lb of digestible protein occurs. Hence $(1.6 - 0.876) \div 0.295 = 0.724 \div 0.295 = 2.45$ lb of cottonseed meal are used in this replacement.

This replacement of 2.45 lb of corn by an equal quantity of cottonseed meal lowers the productive energy content by $2.45(0.848 - 0.749) = 2.45 \times 0.099 = 0.24$ therm. Addition of 0.3 lb of corn restores this amount of productive energy and does not seriously affect the bulk nor the digestible protein content.

The quantities of the specified feeds required for this ration are about as follows:

Feed	Pounds
Cottonseed hulls .... $24 - 13 =$	11.0
Corn .... $13 - 2.45 + 0.3 =$	10.85
Cottonseed meal	2.45
Total bulk	24.30

This example may be solved by forming and solving a system of equations. If x, y, and z denote, respectively, the number of pounds each of hulls, corn, and cottonseed meal, we obtain the following three equations:

(1) $x + y + z = 24.$

(2) $0.004x + 0.064y + 0.359z = 1.6.$

(3) $0.179x + 0.848y + 0.749z = 13.$

Equations (1), (2), and (3) are based upon the ration requirements of bulk, digestible protein, and productive energy, respectively. The results obtained by solving this system differ little from those obtained by the trial replacement method.

In formulating a ration on the basis of bulk, protein, and energy requirements, only one combination of three specified feeds is possible; but, if more than three feeds are to be used in the mixture, many satisfactory combinations can usually be worked out.

4. On the basis of content of digestible protein only, (a) what would be a fair price per bushel to pay for oats if corn is worth 60¢ per bushel? (b) Compare the value of 100 lb of oats with the value of 100 lb of corn.

(a)   1 bu of corn contains $56 \times 0.064 = 3.584$ lb of digestible protein. 1 bu of oats contains $32 \times 0.096 = 3.072$ lb of digestible protein.

A bushel of oats then should be worth $\dfrac{3.072}{3.584} \times 60¢$, or 51.4¢.

(b)   100 lb of corn contains 6.4 lb of digestible protein, while 100 lb of oats contains 9.6 lb of digestible protein. Then oats should be worth 9.6/6.4, or 1.5, times as much per 100 lb as corn. If corn is worth 60¢ per bushel, it is worth about $1.07 per hundredweight, and oats should be worth about $1.60 per hundredweight.

Problems

1. Determine the nutritive ratio of each of these feeds: (a) corn, (b) oats, (c) alfalfa leaf meal, (d) cottonseed meal.

2. On the basis of total digestible nutrients only, compare the values of equal weights of corn and oats. If corn is worth 80¢ per bushel, what should oats be worth per hundredweight?

3. How many pounds of corn are required to provide as much digestible protein as is contained in 100 lb of cottonseed meal?

4. How many pounds of Sudan grass hay provide as much productive energy as that supplied by 100 lb of ground oats?

5. How many pounds each of corn and cottonseed meal are required for the two together to provide digestible protein and productive energy equivalent to that provided by 100 lb of wheat bran?

6. Compute the nutritive ratio of a horse and mule feed consisting of the following: corn, 70 lb; oats, 15 lb; cottonseed meal, 7 lb; molasses, 7 lb; and salt, 1 lb.

7. Commercial mixed feeds usually bear tags indicating analyses guaranteed by manufacturers. Such an analysis shows approximately the per cents of crude protein, crude fat, crude fiber, and nitrogen-free extract present in the feed. Work out an analysis of this kind for the following poultry-fattening mixture: corn, 34 lb; wheat gray shorts, 20 lb; kafir chops, 20 lb; dried buttermilk, 15 lb; ground oats, 10 lb; and salt, 1 lb.

8. Determine the nutritive ratio of a dairy cow feed consisting of the following: cottonseed meal, 20 lb; corn meal, 33 lb; wheat bran, 15 lb; ground whole oats, 12 lb; molasses, 12 lb; alfalfa leaf meal, 5 lb; ground limestone, 2 lb; and salt, 1 lb.

9. Compute the number of therms of productive energy supplied by the 100 lb of feed described in Problem 8. If a dairy cow is fed 3 lb of this mixture for each gallon of milk she produces, how many therms of productive energy are provided per day by this feed for a cow that is producing 4 gal of milk daily?

10. Determine the nutritive ratio of a hog feed consisting of 88 lb of corn meal and 6 lb each of tankage and cottonseed meal.

11. Find approximately the number of pounds each of corn, cottonseed meal, and cottonseed hulls required to form a ration whose bulk is about 20 lb and which provides 1.5 lb of digestible protein and 12 therms of productive energy.

12. Compute the nutritive ratio of the following poultry scratch feed: corn, 40 lb; kafir, 30 lb; wheat, 20 lb; and barley, 10 lb.

13. Formulate a suitable ration for a 500-lb growing (and fattening) steer, basing the requirements on the standards given in Table X and selecting feeds from those listed in Table IX.

14. Work out a suitable ration for a 1200-lb horse at medium work, referring to Tables IX and X for needed data.

15. Work out a suitable ration for a 900-lb dairy cow which is producing 4 gal of 5% milk daily.

16. Suppose that 100 lb of live-weight pork can be produced from 700 lb of shelled corn or from a mixture consisting of 300 lb of shelled corn, 25 lb of tankage, and 25 lb of cottonseed meal. If shelled corn is worth $1.40 per bushel, and cottonseed meal is worth $4.50 per hundredweight, how much could a feeder afford to pay for tankage so that the cost of pork production from feeding the mixture would not exceed the cost from feeding corn alone?

17. How many pounds of cottonseed supply as much digestible protein as is contained in 100 lb of cottonseed meal?

18. How many pounds each of corn and cottonseed meal fed together are equivalent to 100 lb of ground oats in the amounts of digestible protein and productive energy provided?

19. As sources of digestible protein only, compare the costs of tankage at $90 per ton and cottonseed meal at $64 per ton.

20. As a source of productive energy only, what should wheat gray shorts be worth per hundredweight when corn is selling at 90¢ per bushel?

Fertilizers

As previously stated, the main plant foods added to soil by applications of fertilizers are nitrogen, phosphoric acid (P_2O_5), and potash.

A prepared fertilizer is usually described by indicating in per cents its content of these three ingredients. For example, a fertilizer is properly designated as a "4–8–6 fertilizer" if 4% of it by weight is nitrogen, 8% is available phosphoric acid, and 6% is potash.

The following examples will illustrate methods of solving certain types of problems included in this chapter. In problems pertaining to valuations of fertilizers, the monetary worth of a fertilizer will be considered as identical with the total value of its plant food content.

Examples

1. Determine the three largest whole numbers proportional to 1, 3, and 1, representing, respectively, the per cents of nitrogen, phosphoric acid, and potash, obtainable for a fertilizer formed from cyanamid testing 22% nitrogen, superphosphate testing 18% phosphoric acid, and muriate of potash testing 50% potash.

It is convenient to consider data regarding 100 lb of fertilizer.

Let x = the number of pounds of nitrogen in 100 lb of this fertilizer.

Then $\dfrac{x}{0.22}$ = the number of pounds of cyanamid required to furnish the x lb of nitrogen,

$3x$ = the number of pounds of phosphoric acid in 100 lb of this fertilizer,

and $\dfrac{3x}{0.18}$ = the number of pounds of superphosphate required to furnish the $3x$ lb of phosphoric acid.

Also x = the number of pounds of potash in 100 lb of the fertilizer,

and $\dfrac{x}{0.50}$ = the number of pounds of muriate of potash required to furnish the x lb of potash.

Now, since as little filler as possible is to be used, the sum

$$\frac{x}{0.22} + \frac{3x}{0.18} + \frac{x}{0.50}$$

is to be as near 100 as is possible with x an integer. If

$$\frac{x}{0.22} + \frac{3x}{0.18} + \frac{x}{0.50} = 100,$$

then $$\frac{x}{22} + \frac{x}{6} + \frac{x}{50} = 1,$$

or $$75x + 275x + 33x = 1650.$$

Adding, we obtain $$383x = 1650.$$

Therefore $$x = 4.3, \text{ approximately.}$$

But x is an integer. Therefore $x = 4$ and $3x = 12$. Hence a 4-12-4 fertilizer can be formed from the specified materials. The student may show that about 7 lb of each 100 lb of this fertilizer must be filler.

2. If nitrogen is worth 12¢ per pound, available phosphoric acid is worth 6¢ per pound, and potash is worth 5¢ per pound, what should be the value of 1 ton of 6-8-4 fertilizer?

6% of 2000 = 120, number of pounds of nitrogen.

120 × \$0.12 = \$14.40, value of nitrogen.

8% of 2000 = 160, number of pounds of phosphoric acid.

160 × \$0.06 = \$9.60, value of phosphoric acid.

4% of 2000 = 80, number of pounds of potash.

80 × \$0.05 = \$4, value of potash.

\$14.40 + \$9.60 + \$4 = \$28, value of 1 ton of this fertilizer.

3. Suppose that on the basis of costs of unmixed fertilizer materials it is estimated that nitrogen is worth 10¢ per pound, available phosphoric acid is worth 6¢ per pound, and potash is worth 4¢ per pound. Assuming that the costs per pound of the three plant foods present in prepared fertilizers are proportional, respectively, to these values, determine the price paid for each of the three plant foods in a 4-8-6 fertilizer retailing at \$36 per ton.

Let x = the number of cents paid per pound of nitrogen,

y = the number of cents paid per pound of phosphoric acid,

z = the number of cents paid per pound of potash.

4% of 2000 = 80, number of pounds of nitrogen in 1 ton.

8% of 2000 = 160, number of pounds of phosphoric acid in 1 ton.

6% of 2000 = 120, number of pounds of potash in 1 ton.

Then $$80x + 160y + 120z = 3600,$$

or (1) $$2x + 4y + 3z = 90.$$

Also, $$\frac{x}{y} = \frac{10}{6},$$

or (2) $$y = \frac{3x}{5},$$

and $$\frac{x}{z} = \frac{10}{4},$$

or (3) $$z = \frac{2x}{5}.$$

Using (2) and (3) to substitute for y and z in (1), we obtain

$$2x + \frac{12x}{5} + \frac{6x}{5} = 90,$$

or
$$10x + 12x + 6x = 450.$$

Adding, we obtain
$$28x = 450.$$

Therefore $\quad x = 16.07$, approximately.

From (2) $\quad y = \dfrac{3(16.07)}{5} = \dfrac{48.21}{5} = 9.64$, approximately.

From (3) $\quad z = \dfrac{2(16.07)}{5} = \dfrac{32.14}{5} = 6.43$, approximately.

The prices paid per pound of plant food, then, are approximately 16.1¢ for nitrogen, 9.6¢ for available phosphoric acid, and 6.4¢ for potash.

Problems

1. How many pounds each of nitrate of soda, superphosphate (18%), and muriate of potash are required in making a ton of 6-8-4 fertilizer? How much filler is needed?

2. Determine the per cent of each of the three main plant foods present in a prepared fertilizer consisting of 840 lb of superphosphate (18%), 1000 lb of cottonseed meal, and 160 lb of muriate of potash.

3. How many pounds each of superphosphate (20%) and cottonseed meal are present in a ton of fertilizer testing 4% nitrogen and 8% available phosphoric acid? What per cent of the mixture is potash?

4. If nitrogen, available phosphoric acid, and potash in fertilizers are considered worth, respectively, 14¢, 7¢, and 6¢ per pound, what should be the cost of 4-8-4 fertilizer to be applied to 60 acres of corn land at the rate of 250 lb per acre?

5. If 400 lb of a 6-8-4 fertilizer are mixed with 600 lb of a 4-12-4 fertilizer, what are the per cents of the three plant foods in the mixture?

6. Determine the three largest whole numbers, proportional to 1, 2, and 1 and indicating, respectively, the per cents of nitrogen, phosphoric acid, and potash, obtainable for a fertilizer to be formed from nitrate of soda, superphosphate (20%), and muriate of potash.

7. In comparing valuations of fertilizers in 1939–1940 the Texas Agricultural Experiment Station used the following approximate average costs per pound of plant food: 12.0¢ for nitrogen, 6.5¢ for available phosphoric acid, and 6.0¢ for potash. At these prices what would be a fair price per ton to pay for 6-10-7 fertilizer?

8. If the prices paid per pound of nitrogen, available phosphoric acid, and potash are proportional, respectively, to the average costs given in

Problem 7, what price is paid per pound for each of the plant foods if $36 is paid for a ton of 4-10-4 fertilizer?

9. How much 4-8-4 fertilizer contains the same amount of each of the plant foods as a ton of 6-12-6 fertilizer? If 6-12-6 fertilizer is worth $36 per ton, what should 4-8-4 fertilizer be considered worth?

10. Is it more economical to buy 4-12-4 fertilizer at $32 per ton or 5-15-5 fertilizer at $38 per ton?

11. If 800 lb of cottonseed meal are added to a ton of 3-10-3 fertilizer, what per cent of each of the plant foods is contained in the resulting mixture?

12. Determine the per cent of each of the plant foods in a sack of fertilizer containing 25 lb of nitrate of soda, 67 lb of superphosphate (20%), and 8 lb of muriate of potash.

13. Determine the three largest whole numbers, proportional to 1-3-1 and indicating, respectively, the per cents of nitrogen, phosphoric acid, and potash, obtainable for a fertilizer to be formed from sulfate of ammonia, superphosphate (20%), and sulfate of potash.

14. At the average costs per pound of plant food given in Problem 7, what should be the value of a fertilizer consisting of 800 lb of superphosphate (18%), 800 lb of cottonseed meal, 200 lb of nitrate of soda, and 200 lb of muriate of potash?

15. Compute the quantity of each of the following plant food carriers required in making a ton of 4-10-4 fertilizer: sulfate of ammonia furnishing the nitrogen, superphosphate (20%) supplying the phosphoric acid, and kainit and muriate of potash together furnishing the potash in such quantities that no filler is required.

Mixtures

Formulas

If a person is engaged in work that requires the solving of a great number of mixture problems of the same kind, he saves time by using a formula instead of setting up and solving a system of equations for each problem. The formula is derived from a system of equations for solving a general type of mixture problem.

Consider the problem of finding the number of pounds each of milk testing $r_1\%$ butterfat and milk testing $r_2\%$ butterfat required to make N lb of milk testing $r\%$ butterfat. Without loss of generality we may assume that r_2 is greater than r_1.

Let $N_1 =$ the number of pounds of milk testing $r_1\%$ required,
and $N_2 =$ the number of pounds of milk testing $r_2\%$ required.

We may now write the following system of equations:

(1) $N_1 + N_2 = N.$

(2) $r_1 N_1 + r_2 N_2 = rN.$

Multiplying each member of Equation (1) by r_2 and subtracting the corresponding members of Equation (2), we have

$$r_2 N_1 + r_2 N_2 = r_2 N.$$
$$r_1 N_1 + r_2 N_2 = rN.$$
$$\overline{(r_2 - r_1)N_1 = (r_2 - r)N.}$$

(a) $N_1 = \dfrac{r_2 - r}{r_2 - r_1} N.$

In like manner, we may eliminate N_1 and find

(b) $N_2 = \dfrac{r - r_1}{r_2 - r_1} N.$

Formulas (a) and (b) express the values of N_1 and N_2 in terms of numbers that are known, and the solution of a particular problem of this type is obtained at once by making proper substitutions for letters in the right-hand side of each formula.

The Mixture Lever

If each member of Formula (a) is divided by the corresponding member of Formula (b), the result is the proportion

$$\frac{N_1}{N_2} = \frac{r_2 - r}{r - r_1}.$$

Various devices are used to help the student remember this proportion or to suggest to him certain manipulations involved in its application. One such device is the *"mixture lever,"* so called because it employs a principle analogous to that of the balanced lever.

The proportion

$$\frac{N_1}{N_2} = \frac{r_2 - r}{r - r_1}$$

may be associated with a lever in the following way. On a straight-line segment representing a lever, the per cent r of butterfat in the final mixture is placed at a point corresponding to the fulcrum of the lever; and the numbers of pounds, N_1 and N_2, of the component parts of the mixture are then placed on the line segment at points whose distances from the fulcrum are such that the per cent differences $r - r_1$ and $r_2 - r$ may be interpreted as the lever arms of N_1 and N_2, respectively. See Fig. 87.

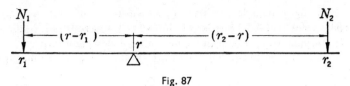

Fig. 87

The equation
$$\frac{N_1}{N_2} = \frac{r_2 - r}{r - r_1}$$

then conforms to the principle of the lever.

Written in the form
$$N_1(r - r_1) + N_2(r - r_2) = 0,$$

this equation may be extended as a formula to cover the case in which several quantities of milk testing different per cents of butterfat are mixed. If m such quantities, N_1 lb, N_2 lb, N_3 lb, . . . , N_m lb, of milk testing $r_1\%$, $r_2\%$, $r_3\%$, . . . , $r_m\%$ of butterfat, respectively, are mixed, we have

$$N_1(r - r_1) + N_2(r - r_2) + N_3(r - r_3) + \ldots + N_m(r - r_m) = 0.$$

In a particular problem the value of any one of the letters involved in this equation may be found, provided that the values of all of the other letters are known.

Example

A mixture is formed of 50 lb of milk testing 6% butterfat, 80 lb testing 4.5%, 100 lb testing 4%, and 60 lb testing 3.5%. The mixture should contain what per cent of butterfat?

Let $r =$ the per cent of butterfat in the mixture.
Then
$$50(r - 6) + 80(r - 4.5) + 100(r - 4) + 60(r - 3.5) = 0,$$
or
$$50r - 300 + 80r - 360 + 100r - 400 + 60r - 210 = 0.$$
Collecting terms, we obtain
$$290r = 1270, \quad \text{and} \quad r = 4.4 \quad \text{approximately.}$$
The mixture contains therefore approximately 4.4% butterfat.

Problems

1. A mixture formed from 80 lb of milk testing 5.2% butterfat and 120 lb testing 3.5% butterfat should contain what per cent butterfat?

2. How many pounds of milk testing 6% butterfat should be added to the mixture mentioned in Problem 1 to raise the butterfat content to 5%?

3. How many pounds of nitrate of soda testing 16% nitrogen should be added to 500 lb of 2-8-4 fertilizer to form a fertilizer testing 4% nitrogen?

4. Determine the per cent of protein in the following mixture for dairy cows: 400 lb of corn meal, 200 lb of wheat bran, and 400 lb of cottonseed meal.

5. A milk distributor formed a mixture consisting of the following lots of milk bought from producers: 150 lb testing 4.5% butterfat, 210 lb testing 3% butterfat, 100 lb testing 4% butterfat, and 80 lb testing 5.3% butterfat. What per cent butterfat was contained in the mixture?

Insurable Value of Farm Buildings

Most insurance companies try to insure farm buildings at about 80% of the *present cash value*. The *present cash value* is usually defined as the replacement cost new less a reasonable amount of depreciation. The replacement cost new is obtained from the size of the structure and the current cost per square foot of floor area or per cubic foot of volume. The per cent of yearly depreciation is found by dividing 100 by the total number of years of expected life of the new structure.

Example

Determine the insurable value of a 15-yr-old barn 60 ft long, 36 ft wide, and 16 ft high if a new similar structure is estimated to cost $4.80 per square foot of floor area and would be expected to last for 50 yr.

$$\text{Floor area} = 60 \times 36 = 2160 \text{ sq ft.}$$

$$\text{Replacement cost new} = 2160 \times 4.80 = \$10,368.00.$$

$$\text{Per cent yearly depreciation} = \frac{100}{50} = 2\%.$$

$$\text{Total depreciation} = 0.02 \times 10,368.00 \times 15 = \$3110.40.$$

$$\text{Present cash value} = \$10,368.00 - \$3110.40 = \$7257.60.$$

$$\text{Insurable value} = 0.80 \times \$7257.60 = \$5806.08.$$

Problems

1. Determine approximately the insurable value of a 5-room farm dwelling measuring 55 by 28 ft, with 9-ft walls, if the building is 8 yr old and a new similar structure is estimated to cost $7.50 per square foot of floor space and would be expected to last 60 yr.

2. Find the approximate insurable value of a box-shaped barn 60 ft long, 34 ft wide, and 24 ft tall if the barn was built 12 yr ago and its replacement cost new is estimated at 16⅔¢ per cubic foot, the life expectancy of the new structure being 40 yr.

3. A 7-yr-old poultry house has a 24-ft square foundation and 10-ft walls. Cost of replacement new is estimated at $2.52 per square foot of floor space, and a new structure would be expected to last 35 yr. Determine the insurable value of the poultry house.

4. Find the insurable value of a 2-car garage 18 by 20 ft, with 10-ft walls, if it is 5 yr old and if it is estimated that a new one of similar construction would cost $1080 and would last 30 yr.

5. Assuming new construction cost at $0.20 per cubic foot and a 40-yr life expectancy for a new structure, estimate the present value of a dairy barn 50 ft long and 34 ft wide, with 20-ft walls and a ¼-pitch gable roof running lengthwise of the building, if the barn is now 15 years old?

Work, Energy, and Power

In physics the word *work* is used in the following restricted sense. If a force F acting on a body causes it to move a distance d in the direction of the force, work is said to be done, and is measured by the product of the numbers of units in F and d. A standard unit of measure of work is the foot-pound, which is defined as the work done by a force of 1 lb in moving a body a distance of 1 ft in the direction of the force. Thus if a body weighing 5 lb is lifted vertically through a distance of 3 ft, the work done is 15 ft-lb.

Energy, defined as any sort of capacity for doing work and appearing in various forms (including heat) is measured in terms of the units used in measuring work.

Power is defined as the time rate at which work is done. One standard unit of measure of power is the horsepower (hp) which is defined as the rate of 550 ft-lb of work per second. Thus if a body weighing 21 lb is lifted to a height of 25 ft in 2 sec, the average power is $25 \times 21 \div 2$, or 137.5 ft-lb per second, which may be expressed as ¼ hp.

In considering the performance of a machine in doing work the energy required by the machine is referred to as "work input," and the work delivered by the machine as "work output." The *efficiency* of a machine in doing a piece of work is defined as the ratio of its work output to its work input, and is usually expressed as a per cent. Thus, if a force of 30 lb acting along an inclined plane elevates a 50-lb block 10 ft by sliding it up the plane a distance of 20 ft, the work output is 50×10, or 500 ft-lb, the work-input is 30×20, or 600 ft-lb, and the efficiency of the machine is ⅚ or $83\frac{1}{3}\%$.

Problems

1. Show that the weight of a vertical column of water h feet tall and having a cross section of 1 sq in. is approximately $0.434h$ lb. This indicates about the force per square inch exerted by a pump in lifting water from a well h ft deep.

2. Find the total force exerted by a pump in lifting water from a 240-ft well through a cylinder $1\frac{1}{2}$ in. in diameter.

3. Find the work output of a pump in delivering 1000 gal of water from the well of Problem 2. If the pump has an efficiency rating of 60%, what work input does it require per 1000 gal of water delivered?

4. How many foot-pounds of work are done in elevating 12 tons of hay from an average level of 10 ft above the ground to an average level of 25 ft above the ground?

5. Estimate the amount of work in foot-pounds expended by a silage blower in filling a cylindrical silo 14 ft in diameter and 40 ft tall, assuming the silage to weigh 40 lb per cubic foot and to be lifted from a height of 5 ft above the ground to an average height of 20 ft above the ground, and assuming further that only 25% of the energy expended by the machine is effective in elevating silage.

6. Find the actual work realized or accomplished in lifting 2000 gal of water from a well 240 ft deep to an average level of 30 ft above the ground. If the pump lifting this water expends energy which is only 60% effective in lifting water, find the total energy expended by the pump.

7. With a 6-pulley block-and-tackle arrangement, a 500-lb piece of equipment is lifted 8 ft vertically by applying a 90-lb force through a distance of 48 ft. Find the efficiency of this hoist.

8. At what rate (expressed as horsepower) is work being done by a pump in delivering 10 gal of water per minute from a well 300 ft deep?

9. If the pump of the preceding problem has an efficiency of 50%, it would require a motor of what power rating to drive it?

10. Assuming that the 1.5 hp delivered by this motor is 75% of the power the motor draws from an electric power line, find the approximate cost, at 3¢ per kilowatt-hour, of electric energy required to operate the pump for 1 hr.

11. Using the data of the several related problems above, estimate the electric energy cost per 1000 gal of water delivered by the pump of Problem 10.

12. Rates at which electric motors of various horsepower delivery ratings may be expected to consume electric energy are:

Motor hp	$\frac{1}{2}$	1	2	3	5	$7\frac{1}{2}$	10
Consumption rate (watts)	530	1,060	1,865	2,795	4,415	6,870	9,325

Compute the efficiency of each motor and make a curve graph showing variation of efficiency (expressed as per cent) with size of motor.

CHAPTER 10

EXPONENTS; LOGARITHMS; THE SLIDE RULE

Exponents

Exponents play an important role in the development of certain processes and devices used to shorten the work of multiplication, division, computation of powers, and extraction of roots. For this reason, a brief review of the definitions and laws of exponents is given here.

In the following tables m and n denote positive integers and a, b, and c represent numbers different from zero.

Definitions	*Examples*	
1. $a^n = a \cdot a \cdot a \cdots a$ (n factors).	$a^3 = a \cdot a \cdot a.$	$5^3 = 5 \cdot 5 \cdot 5 = 125.$
2. $a^{-n} = \dfrac{1}{a^n}.$	$a^{-3} = \dfrac{1}{a^3}.$	$5^{-3} = \dfrac{1}{5^3} = \dfrac{1}{125}.$
3. $a^{\frac{m}{n}} = \sqrt[n]{a^m}.$	$a^{\frac{2}{3}} = \sqrt[3]{a^2}.$	$5^{\frac{2}{3}} = \sqrt[3]{5^2}.$
4. $a^0 = 1.$	$a^0 = 1.$	$5^0 = 1.$

Laws	*Examples*	
1. $a^m \cdot a^n = a^{m+n}.$	$a^3 \cdot a^2 = a^5.$	$2^3 \cdot 2^2 = 2^5 = 32.$
2. $\dfrac{a^m}{a^n} = a^{m-n}.$	$\dfrac{a^5}{a^2} = a^{5-2} = a^3.$	$\dfrac{2^5}{2^2} = 2^{5-2} = 2^3 = 8.$
3. $(a^m)^n = a^{mn}.$	$(a^2)^3 = a^6.$	$(2^2)^3 = 2^6 = 64.$
4. $(abc)^n = a^n b^n c^n.$	$(abc)^3 = a^3 b^3 c^3.$	$(3bc^2)^2 = 9b^2 c^4.$
5. $\left(\dfrac{a}{b}\right)^n = \dfrac{a^n}{b^n}.$	$\left(\dfrac{a}{b}\right)^4 = \dfrac{a^4}{b^4}.$	$\left(\dfrac{2}{3}\right)^4 = \dfrac{2^4}{3^4} = \dfrac{16}{81}.$

Logarithms

In the statement $2^3 = 8$, 2 is regarded as the *base*, 3 is an *exponent* (or *exponent of power*), and 2^3, or 8, is called a *power* of 2. Also, the exponent 3 is called the *logarithm* of 8 with respect to the base 2 and is denoted by $\log_2 8$. In general, if $a^x = N$, then x is called the logarithm of N with respect to the base a. Symbolically, we write, $\log_a N = x$.

Since a logarithm is an exponent, certain properties of logarithms are derived from the laws of exponents. These properties and their connection with the laws of exponents are exhibited in the following table. In this table, M and N denote positive numbers and a is a positive number other than 1.

Laws of Exponents	*Properties of Logarithms*
I. If $M = a^x$ and $N = a^y$, then $MN = a^x a^y = a^{x+y}$.	I. $\log_a MN = \log_a M + \log_a N$.
II. If $M = a^x$ and $N = a^y$, then $\dfrac{M}{N} = \dfrac{a^x}{a^y} = a^{x-y}$.	II. $\log_a \dfrac{M}{N} = \log_a M - \log_a N$.
III. If $M = a^x$, then $M^p = (a^x)^p = a^{px}$ and $\sqrt[q]{M} = M^{\frac{1}{q}} = (a^x)^{\frac{1}{q}} = a^{\frac{x}{q}}$.	III. $\log_a M^p = p \log_a M$ and $\log_a \sqrt[q]{M} = \dfrac{1}{q} \log_a M$.

For the purpose of shortening the work in certain arithmetical computations it is convenient to consider all positive numbers as powers of 10. By methods not within the scope of this book it is possible to determine to a required number of decimal places the logarithm of any positive number with respect to the base 10. In other words, if N denotes a positive number, a number x can be found so that $10^x = N$ within any range of approximation desired. (In this book, log N means $\log_{10} N$.)

In the first column of the table on page 163 are listed certain numbers, and in the second column opposite each of these numbers is given the logarithm of that number with respect to the base 10. Explanations given in the third column are intended to make clear the connection between a number and its logarithm but not to suggest a general method for obtaining logarithms.

Number	Logarithm	Explanation
0.001	-3	$10^{-3} = \dfrac{1}{10^3} = \dfrac{1}{1000} = 0.001.$
0.01	-2	$10^{-2} = \dfrac{1}{10^2} = \dfrac{1}{100} = 0.01.$
0.1	-1	$10^{-1} = \dfrac{1}{10^1} = \dfrac{1}{10} = 0.1.$
1	0	$10^0 = 1.$
2.1544	$\tfrac{1}{3}$	$10^{\frac{1}{3}} = \sqrt[3]{10} = 2.1544$, approximately.
3.1623	$\tfrac{1}{2}$	$10^{\frac{1}{2}} = \sqrt{10} = 3.1623$, approximately.
4.6416	$\tfrac{2}{3}$	$10^{\frac{2}{3}} = \sqrt[3]{10^2} = \sqrt[3]{100} = 4.6416$, approximately.
10	1	$10^1 = 10.$
31.623	$\tfrac{3}{2}$	$10^{\frac{3}{2}} = \sqrt{10^3} = \sqrt{1000} = 31.623$, approximately.
100	2	$10^2 = 100.$
316.23	$\tfrac{5}{2}$	$10^{\frac{5}{2}} = \sqrt{10^5} = \sqrt{100,000} = 316.23$, approximately.
1000	3	$10^3 = 1000.$
3162.3	$\tfrac{7}{2}$	$10^{\frac{7}{2}} = \sqrt{10^7} = \sqrt{10,000,000} = 3162.3$, approximately.
10,000	4	$10^4 = 10,000.$

The significant figures of a number include the first nonzero figure at the left and all the figures that follow it.   If two numbers are made up of the same sequence of significant figures but differ in the position of the decimal point, then their logarithms to the base 10 differ by a whole number.   Thus, $3162.3 = 100 \times 31.623$.   By Property I, log $3162.3 = \log 100 + \log 31.623 = 2 + \log 31.623$.   In the above table note that $\log 31.623 = 1.5$, and $\log 3162.3 = 3.5$.   The property just mentioned makes it desirable to express a logarithm that is not a whole number as a *sum* of an *integer* (positive or negative) and a *positive decimal fraction*.   The integer thus involved is called the *characteristic* of the logarithm, and the positive decimal fraction is called the *mantissa* of the logarithm.   Thus the characteristic of the logarithm of 3162.3 is 3, and the mantissa is .5.   Table XII, page 201, gives to four decimal places the mantissas of logarithms of numbers up to 1000.   The characteristic of the logarithm of a number is readily determined by inspection.   From the above table observe that numbers between 1 and 10 have logarithms between 0 and 1, and each such logarithm has 0 for its characteristic; numbers between 10 and 100 have logarithms between 1 and 2, and each such logarithm has 1 as its characteristic; numbers between 100 and 1000 have logarithms between 2 and 3, and each such logarithm has 2 for its characteristic; and so on. A rule may now be stated: *If a number is greater than 1, the characteristic of its logarithm is positive, or zero, and is one less than the number of significant digits to the left of the decimal point.*

Numbers between 0.1 and 1 have logarithms between -1 and 0, and each such logarithm, being the sum of a *positive decimal* fraction and a *whole* number, has -1 for its characteristic; numbers between 0.01 and 0.1 have logarithms between -2 and -1, and each such logarithm has -2 for its characteristic; numbers between 0.001 and 0.01 have logarithms between -3 and -2, and each such logarithm has -3 for its characteristic; and so on. These facts suggest this rule: *If a number is expressed as a positive decimal fraction, the characteristic of its logarithm is negative and is numerically one more than the number of zeros immediately following the decimal point.*

Use of Table of Mantissas

As already pointed out, numbers consisting of the same sequence of figures have the same mantissa in their logarithms. It follows, too, that zeros contained at the extreme right in a number may be disregarded in determining a mantissa. Thus 6, 60, and 600 have the same mantissa in their logarithms, and this mantissa, .7782, is listed in Table XII in the column headed by 0 and is opposite the 60 of the N column. The mantissas of the logarithms of all one-digit and two-digit numbers are listed in the column headed by 0. The mantissa of the logarithm of a *three-digit* number is found in the column headed by the third digit of the number and is opposite the entry of the other two digits in the N column. Consult the table and check these values: $\log 3.5 = 0.5441$; $\log 35 = 1.5441$; $\log 350 = 2.5441$; $\log 356 = 2.5514$; $\log 357 = 2.5527$. Note that $\log 0.356 = -1 + .5514$; and, while this could be written as $-.4486$, it is more convenient to express the -1 as $9 - 10$ and to write $\log 0.356 = 9.5514 - 10$. Similarly, $\log 0.00356 = -3 + .5514 = 7.5514 - 10$.

In determining the mantissa of the logarithm of a number consisting of more than three digits, the first and last of which are different from zero, it is convenient to place temporarily a decimal point after the first three digits and consider the number as being between two three-digit numbers listed in the table. An example will illustrate: Consider $\log 35.642$. The characteristic of $\log 35.642$ is 1. The mantissa is the same as that for

356.42 and is considered as 0.42 of the way between the mantissa of log 356 and that of 357.

Number   Mantissa

$$
1\left\{\begin{array}{l}\text{Increase}\\357\\0.42\left\{\begin{array}{l}356.42\\356\end{array}\right.\end{array}\right.
\quad
\begin{array}{l}0.5527\\?\\0.5514\end{array}
\left.\begin{array}{l}\\\\\end{array}\right\}
\begin{array}{l}\text{Increase}\\0.0013\end{array}
$$

0.42 of 0.0013 = 0.000546

An increase of 1 in the number is accompanied by an increase of .0013 in the mantissa; then an increase of 0.42 in the number should be accompanied by an increase of approximately 0.42 of .0013, which is .000546, or about .0005. Hence the mantissa of log 356.42 is .5514+.0005, or .5519, and log 35.642 = 1.5519.

In finding a number whose logarithm is known, the sequence of figures making up the number is obtained by locating as nearly as possible the mantissa of the given logarithm in Table XII; the position of the decimal point is then determined by seeing that the characteristic of the given logarithm conforms to the rules previously given for characteristics.

Suppose that log N = 1.8993. What number is N? In Table XII, .8993 is found to be the mantissa of the logarithm of all numbers having the sequence of figures 793. Since the characteristic of log N is 1, it follows that N = 79.3.

If log A = 2.8993, then A = 793.
If log B = 3.8993, then B = 7930.
If log C = 0.8993, then C = 7.93.
If log D = 9.8993 − 10, then D = 0.793.
If log E = 8.8993 − 10, then E = 0.0793.

Next suppose that log M = 1.8996. The mantissa .8996 is not given in Table XII.

$$
0.0005\left\{\begin{array}{l}0.0003\left\{\begin{array}{l}1.8993=\log 79.3\\1.8996=\log M\end{array}\right.\\[1em]1.8998=\log 79.4\end{array}\right.
\left.\begin{array}{l}\\\\\end{array}\right\}0.1
$$

It seems reasonable to conclude that M is between 79.3 and 79.4 and further that M is approximately three-fifths of the way from 79.3 to 79.4.

$\frac{3}{5}$ of 0.1 = 0.06.

Therefore M = 79.3 + 0.06 = 79.36, approximately.

Problems

Without the use of a table, find the value of the letter involved in each of the following:

1. $5^x = 25.$

2. $\log_5 25 = X.$

3. $\log_3 N = 4.$

4. $\log_a 8 = 3.$

5. $\log_2 32 = X.$

6. $\log_{10} N = 3.$

7. $10^x = 0.001$

8. $\log_{10} 0.001 = X.$

9. $\log_{10} N = 0.$

10. $\log_{10} 10,000 = X.$

By use of Table XII find each of the following:

11. $\log 367.$

12. $\log 3.67.$

13. $\log 0.00367.$

14. $\log 36,700.$

15. $\log 3674.$

16. N if $\log N = 1.6839.$

17. A if $\log A = 2.9542.$

18. B if $\log B = 3.9628.$

19. N if $\log N = 8.7210 - 10.$

20. M if $\log M = 1.4752.$

Computations by Use of Logarithms

A few examples will illustrate how logarithms are useful in obtaining results of multiplication, division, and computations of powers and roots. Since most of the mantissas of logarithms given in Table XII are approximations, the results obtained by use of logarithms are usually only approximately correct. Arrangement of work in the form used here is suggested.

Examples

1. Compute $(36.2)(8.4)$.

Let $\qquad N = (36.2)(8.4).$

Then $\qquad \log N = \log 36.2 + \log 8.4.$

$\qquad \log 36.2 = 1.5587.$

$\qquad \log 8.4 = \underline{0.9243.}$

Adding, $\qquad \log N = 2.4830.$

$\qquad N = 304.1,$ approximately.

2. Compute $\dfrac{574.8}{6.24}.$

Let $\qquad N = \dfrac{574.8}{6.24}.$

Then $\qquad \log N = \log 574.8 - \log 6.24.$

$\qquad \log 574.8 = 2.7595.$

$\qquad \log 6.24 = \underline{0.7952.}$

Subtracting, $\qquad \log N = 1.9643.$

$\qquad N = 92.1,$ approximately.

3. Compute $\dfrac{(0.0258)\,(437)}{60.82}$.

Let $$N = \frac{(0.0258)\,(437)}{60.82}.$$

Then
$$\log N = \log 0.0258 + \log 437 - \log 60.82.$$
$$\log 0.0258 = 8.4116 - 10.$$
$$\log 437 = 2.6405.$$

Adding, $\log$ numerator $= \overline{11.0521 - 10}$, or 1.0521.
$$\log 60.82 = 1.7840.$$

Subtracting, $\log N = \overline{9.2681 - 10.}$
$$N = 0.1854, \text{ approximately.}$$

4. Compute $(83.5)^3$.
Let $N = (83.5)^3.$
Then
$$\log N = 3 \log 83.5$$
$$= 3(1.9217)$$
$$= 5.7651.$$
$$N = 582,200, \text{ approximately.}$$

In this case the last three digits of N cannot be considered accurate. Actual multiplication gives $(83.5)^3 = 582,182.875$. A more extensive table of logarithms could be used to give the degree of accuracy desired.

5. (a) Compute $\sqrt[3]{32.96}$.
Let $N = \sqrt[3]{32.96}.$
Then
$$\log N = \tfrac{1}{3} \log 32.96$$
$$= \tfrac{1}{3}(1.5180)$$
$$= 0.5060.$$
$$N = 3.206, \text{ approximately.}$$

(b) Compute $\sqrt[3]{0.3296}$.
Let $N = \sqrt[3]{0.3296}.$
Then
$$\log N = \tfrac{1}{3} \log 0.3296$$
$$= \tfrac{1}{3}(9.5180 - 10)$$
$$= \tfrac{1}{3}(29.5180 - 30)$$
$$= 9.8393 - 10.$$
$$N = 0.6907.$$

Note that -1 may be written as $29 - 30$ and that, in this case, this form is more convenient than the form $9 - 10$.

6. Compute $\dfrac{(83.5)\,(0.063)^{\frac{2}{3}}}{400\sqrt{51.7}}$.

Let $X = \dfrac{(83.5)\,(0.063)^{\frac{2}{3}}}{400\sqrt{51.7}}.$

Then $\log X = (\log 83.5 + \tfrac{2}{3}\log 0.063) - (\log 400 + \tfrac{1}{2}\log 51.7)$

$\log 83.5 = 1.9217.$

$\tfrac{2}{3}\log 0.063 = \tfrac{2}{3}(8.7993 - 10)$

$= \tfrac{1}{3}(17.5986 - 20)$

$= \tfrac{1}{3}(27.5986 - 30) = 9.1995 - 10.$

Adding, $\log \text{ numerator} = 11.1212 - 10.$

$= 1.1212.$

$\log 400 = 2.6021.$

$\tfrac{1}{2}\log 51.7 = \tfrac{1}{2}(1.7135) = 0.8567.$

Adding, $\log \text{ denominator} = \overline{3.4588.}$

$\log \text{ numerator} = 1.1212 = 11.1212 - 10.$

$\log \text{ denominator} = 3.4588.$

Subtracting,

$\log X = 7.6624 - 10.$

$X = 0.004596.$

Problems

Compute the following by use of logarithms:

1. $(28.4)(3.95)$

2. $(741.8)(0.063)$

3. $\dfrac{35.91}{8.72}$

4. $\dfrac{7.3682}{0.581}$

5. $\dfrac{(83)(6.705)}{429.7}$

6. $(8.37)^3$

7. $\sqrt[5]{16.27}$

8. $(1.5)^{\frac{3}{2}}$

9. $\dfrac{305\sqrt{0.87}}{(37.4)^2}$

10. $\dfrac{(47.28)(0.507)^{\frac{3}{2}}}{0.099\sqrt[3]{12.459}}$

The Slide Rule

As a first step toward explaining the principles and methods employed in the operation of the slide rule, it may be pointed out that results of addition and subtraction of numbers can be obtained mechanically by use of two similar linear scales.   Two 1-ft rules, each graduated in inches, may be used for this purpose.   For convenience, one rule may be referred to as the "M scale" and the other as the "N scale."   To add 3 and 2, place the 0 of the N scale even with the 3 of the M scale and have the scales alongside each other and extending in the same direction.   The 2 of the N scale then falls even with the 5 of the M scale, thus indicating that the sum of 3 and 2 is 5.   To subtract 6 from 10, place the 6 of the N scale even with the 10 of the M scale, keeping the scales alongside each other and extending in the same direction.   The 0 of the N scale is then even with the 4 of the M scale, thus indicating that the difference between 10 and 6 is 4.

As already shown, the product of two numbers can be obtained (at least, approximately) by adding their logarithms and noting the number that has this sum of logarithms as its logarithm.   Also, a quotient of two numbers can be found (approximately) by subtracting the logarithm of the divisor from the logarithm of the dividend and noting the number which has this difference of logarithms as its logarithm.   The student

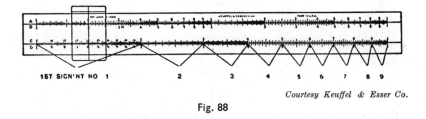

Fig. 88

is reminded that the sequence of significant figures in a product or quotient is determined by the mantissas of the logarithms involved.   The slide rule is a device for performing mechanically the addition and subtraction of mantissas of logarithms involved in computing products and quotients.   The manipulation of the slide rule is similar to the handling of the two 1-ft rules described above.

A slide rule consists essentially of two rules held alongside each other in such a manner that they are free to slide one upon the other in a length-wise direction.   There may be several graduated scales on the rules. Two of these scales, the C scale on one rule and the D scale on the other, are exactly alike.   Instead of being labeled "0," the left end of each of these scales is labeled "1," the number whose logarithm is 0.   The length of the scale is taken as unity, and the position of a number on the scale is determined by the mantissa of the logarithm of the number.   The right end of the scale, also marked "1," may be regarded as corresponding to 1, 10, 100, or to any number whose logarithm has a mantissa equal to 0. Numbers having the same sequence of significant figures have a common mantissa in their logarithms;   hence a position on the C or D scale may be associated with any number whose sequence of significant figures corresponds to that position. Since log 5 = 0.6990, the number 5 appears at a point about 0.7 of the way along the scale. Other numbers that may be associated with this point on the scale are 0.5, 0.05, 50, 500, and so forth.

(a)   The spaces between secondary divisions between the main divisions 1 and 2 are divided into tenths, so that each smallest subdivision counts as one.

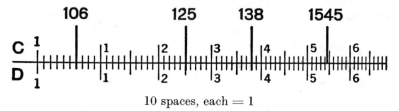

10 spaces, each = 1

(b)   The spaces between secondary divisions between the main divisions 2 and 3 and 3 and 4 are divided into fifths, so that each smallest subdivision counts as two.

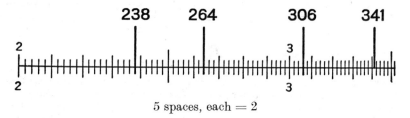

5 spaces, each = 2

(c)   The spaces between secondary divisions for the remainder of the scale are divided only in half, so that each smallest subdivision counts as five.

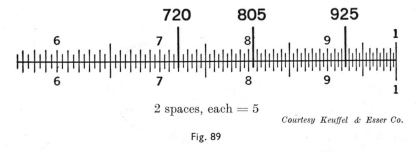

2 spaces, each = 5

Fig. 89

Figure 89, which illustrates sections of the *C* and *D* scales, shows how sequences of figures may be read on the scale.

Recalling the properties of logarithms and the manipulations with the two 1-ft rules, the student will now see how the C and D scales can be used to add and subtract mantissas and to indicate thereby sequences of figures in required products and quotients. The position of the decimal point in a sequence of figures so obtained can be determined by inspection of the numbers involved in the computation. A more detailed explanation of the use of the slide rule will be given in connection with the examples that follow. The slide rule is usually equipped with a movable glass indicator across which there is a hairline perpendicular to the scales. This device is quite helpful to an operator in making settings and readings.

Multiplication
Examples

1. Find the product of 2 and 3.

Align the 1 of the left end of the C scale with the 2 of the D scale. The 3 of the C scale is then in line with the 6 of the D scale, indicating that the product of 2 and 3 is 6. In effect, the logarithms of 2 and 3 have been added, and the 6 is indicated as the number whose logarithm is the sum obtained.

2. Find the product of 4 and 3.

If the *left* 1 of the C scale is aligned with the 4 of the D scale, the 3 of the C scale falls beyond the right end of the D scale, thus indicating that the sum of mantissas involved in this case is greater than 1. The point on the scale corresponding to the mantissa of the logarithm of the product can be found simply by shifting the C scale to the left its full length, thereby aligning the *right* 1 of the C scale with the 4 of the D scale. The 3 of the C scale is then in line with a point on the D scale that corresponds to 1.2, 12, 120, and so forth. Obviously, 12 is the proper reading in this case.

3. Multiply 23 by 7.

Align the *right* 1 of the C scale with the 7 of the D scale. The 23 of the C scale is then in line with the 161 of the D scale.

4. Multiply 2.3 by 7.

The alignment of the scales is the same as for multiplying 23 by 7. In this case, it is evident that the product is less than 100 and greater than 10; hence 16.1 is the proper reading of the product.

5. Multiply 38.4 by 75.

Align the *right* 1 of the C scale with 384 of the D scale. The 75 of the C scale is then in line with 288 of the D scale. The required product is evidently between $30 \times 70 \ (= 2100)$ and $40 \times 80 \ (= 3200)$; hence the correct reading of the product is 2880.

6. Multiply 3.84 by 7.5.

The alignment of the scales is the same as in the preceding example. In this case it is obvious that the result is near 4×7; hence 28.8 is the proper reading of the product.

Problems

By use of the slide rule obtain the following indicated products:

1. (a) (2) (4)
    (b) (20) (4)
    (c) (20) (40)
    (d) (0.2) (4)
    (e) (0.2) (0.04)

2. (a) (6) (7)
    (b) (600) (7)
    (c) (6) (0.7)
    (d) (0.06) (7)
    (e) (0.06) (0.07)

3. (a) (23 (8)
    (b) (2.3) (8)
    (c) (230) (80)
    (d) (0.23) (0.8)
    (e) (0.023) (80)

4. (a) (18) (35)
    (b) (18) (54)
    (c) (18) (65)

5. (a) (350) (23)
    (b) (35) (752)
    (c) (3.5) (75.2)

6. (3.25) (2.1)

7. (π) (14)

8. (525) (6.7)

9. 86% of 1935

10. (635) (0.348) (1.5)

Division

Examples

1. Divide 6 by 3.

Align the 6 of the D scale with the 3 of the C scale. The *left* 1 of the C scale is then in line with the 2 of the D scale, indicating that the quotient is 2. In effect, the logarithm of 3 has been subtracted from the logarithm of 6, and the 2 is indicated as the number whose logarithm is the difference obtained.

2. Divide 35 by 5.

Align the 35 of the D scale with the 5 of the C scale. The *left* 1 of the C scale falls beyond the left end of the D scale, indicating that the mantissa of the logarithm of the divisor 5 is greater than the mantissa of the logarithm of the dividend 35. However, the position on the D scale corresponding to the mantissa of the logarithm of the quotient is now in line with the *right* 1 of the C scale. The quotient 7 is thus indicated.

3. Divide 2880 by 75.

Align the 288 of the D scale with the 75 of the C scale. The *right* 1 of the C scale is then in line with 384 of the D scale. Since $2800 \div 70 = 40$, the quotient $2880 \div 75$ is read as 38.4.

4. Divide 0.072 by 51.6.

Align 516 of the C scale with 72 of the D scale. The *left* 1 of the C scale is then in line with 1395 of the D scale. The quotient $0.072 \div 51.6$ is near $0.07 \div 50$ ($= 0.007 \div 5 = 0.0014$). Hence 0.001395 is taken as the required quotient.

Problems

By use of the slide rule obtain the following indicated quotients:

1. (a) $8 \div 4$
(b) $9 \div 4.5$
(c) $80 \div 40$
(d) $0.8 \div 4$
(e) $0.8 \div 0.04$

2. (a) $75 \div 5$
(b) $7.5 \div 5$
(c) $750 \div 5$
(d) $0.075 \div 0.5$
(e) $75 \div 0.05$

3. (a) $72 \div 144$
(b) $720 \div 144$
(c) $7.2 \div 0.144$

4. (a) $785 \div 54$
(b) $785 \div 5.4$
(c) $7.85 \div 0.054$

5. (a) $248 \div 62$
(b) $0.248 \div 0.62$
(c) $0.0248 \div 6.2$

6. $31.5 \div 16.2$

7. $3.14 \div 2.72$

8. $110 \div \pi$

9. $2875 \div 37.2$

10. $0.685 \div 8.93$

Multiplication and Division

Example

Solve the proportion $\dfrac{x}{6} = \dfrac{36}{24}$.

First obtain the result in the form

$$x = \frac{(36)\,(6)}{24}.$$

Then align 36 of the D scale with 24 of the C scale. The *left* 1 of the C scale is then in line with the quotient $36 \div 24$; hence the 6 of the C scale must be in line with $(6)\,(36 \div 24)$. The final result, 9, is thus read on the D scale from a single setting of the scales.

Problems

Determine the value of x *in each of the following, using the slide rule for multiplication and division:*

1. $\dfrac{x}{6} = \dfrac{42}{36}$.

2. $\dfrac{72}{56} = \dfrac{9}{x}$.

3. $\dfrac{x}{3.6} = \dfrac{2}{3}$.

4. 48 is $x\%$ of 64.

5. $35 = 62.5\%$ of x.

6. 16% of x = 2% of 192.

7. $\dfrac{x}{3.2} = \dfrac{4.6}{80}$.

8. $\dfrac{x}{24} = \dfrac{95}{25.2}$.

9. $x = \dfrac{(23)\,(7)}{(4)\,(12)}$.

10. $x = \dfrac{(4.1)\,(28)\,(92)}{(34)\,(0.81)}$.

Squares and Square Roots

The construction of the A and B scales of the slide rule is similar to that of the C and D scales, except that the unit of length employed is half that used on the C and D scales. The A and D scales are on the *body* of the slide rule, while the B and C scales are on the *slide*. The numbers of the D scale are thus always aligned with their squares on the A scale. Similarly, the numbers of the C scale are in line with their squares on the B scale.

Examples

1. Find the square of 3.

Place the hairline of the indicator over 3 on the D scale and read 9, the square of 3, above on the A scale.

2. Find the square of 25.

Place the hairline over 25 of the D scale and read its square, 625, on the A scale.

3. Find the square of 56.4.

Place the hairline over 564 of the D scale and read 318 above on the A scale. Since $(50)^2 = 2500$ and $(60)^2 = 3600$, the square of 56.4 must have four places to the left of the decimal point. Then $(56.4)^2 = 3180$, approximately. Actually, $(56.4)^2 = 3180.96$.

4. Find the square root of 225.

Set the hairline over 225 of the *left* portion of the A scale and read 15 as the square root on the D scale.

5. Find the square root of 81.

Set the hairline over 81 of the *right* portion of the A scale and read 9 as the square root on the D scale.

In obtaining the square root of a number *greater than 1*, the *left* portion of the A scale is used if the number has an *odd* number of significant figures to the left of the decimal point; otherwise the *right* portion of the A scale is used.

In obtaining the square root of a *decimal fraction*, the *left* portion of the A scale is used if an *odd* number of zeros immediately follows the decimal point; otherwise the *right* portion of the A scale is used.

Problems

By use of the slide rule obtain the following indicated squares and square roots:

1. (a) $(4)^2$
   (b) $(0.4)^2$
   (c) $(40)^2$

2. (a) $(18)^2$
   (b) $(1.8)^2$
   (c) $(0.18)^2$

3. (a) $(24)^2$
   (b) $(24.5)^2$
   (c) $(2.45)^2$

4. (a) $(75)^2$
   (b) $(7.5)^2$
   (c) $(0.75)^2$

5. (a) $(93)^2$
   (b) $(930)^2$
   (c) $(0.093)^2$

6. (a) $\sqrt{9}$
   (b) $\sqrt{0.09}$
   (c) $\sqrt{900}$

7. (a) $\sqrt{81}$
   (b) $\sqrt{0.81}$
   (c) $\sqrt{8.1}$

8. (a) $\sqrt{49}$
   (b) $\sqrt{0.0049}$
   (c) $\sqrt{490}$

9. (a) $\sqrt{256}$
   (b) $\sqrt{2.56}$
   (c) $\sqrt{25.6}$

10. (a) $\sqrt{73.6}$
    (b) $\sqrt{642}$
    (c) $\sqrt{0.0386}$

11. (a) $\sqrt{837}$
    (b) $\sqrt{6.25}$
    (c) $\sqrt{0.0324}$

12. (a) $\sqrt{1.69}$
    (b) $\sqrt{57.4}$
    (c) $\sqrt{72.45}$

TABLES

CES

TABLES

Table I. Measurements

LENGTH (LINEAR MEASURE)

English System

1 hand = 4 inches (in.)
1 foot (ft) = 12 in.
1 vara = 33⅓ in.
1 yard (yd) = 3 ft
1 rod = 5½ yd
= 16½ ft
1 fathom = 6 ft
1 furlong = 40 rods
1 chain = 4 rods
= 22 yd
= 66 ft
1 mile (mi.) = 80 chains
= 320 rods
= 1760 yd
= 1900.8 varas
= 5280 ft

Metric System

1 centimeter (cm) = 10 millimeters (mm)
1 decimeter (dm) = 10 cm
1 meter (m) = 10 dm
= 100 cm
1 kilometer (km) = 1000 m

Approximate Equivalents

1 in. = 2.54 cm
1 ft = 30.480 cm
1 yd = 0.91 m
1 mile = 1.6 km
1 m = 39.37 in.
= 3.3 ft

AREA (SQUARE MEASURE)

English System

1 square foot (sq ft) = 144 square inches (sq in.)
1 square foot (sq ft) = 0.000023 acre
1 square yard (sq yd) = 9 sq ft
1 square rod (sq rd) = 30¼ sq yd
1 square chain (sq chain) = 16 sq rods
1 acre = 10 sq chains
= 160 sq rods
= 4840 sq yd
= 5645.376 sq varas
= 43,560 sq ft
= 6,272,640 sq in.
1 square mile (sq mile) = 640 acres
1 section = 640 acres
1 labor = 1,000,000 sq varas
= 173 acres
1 square league = 25 labors
= 25,000,000 sq varas
= 4428.4 acres

Table I. Measurements (Cont.)

AREA (SQUARE MEASURE)—Cont.

Metric System

1 square centimeter (sq cm or cm²) = 100 square millimeters (sq mm or mm²)

1 square decimeter (sq dm or dm²) = 100 sq cm

1 square meter (sq m or m²) = 100 sq dm

VOLUME (CUBIC MEASURE)

English System

1 cubic foot (cu ft) = 1728 cubic inches (cu in.)

1 cubic yard (cu yd) = 27 cu ft

1 cord (cd) = 128 cu ft

Metric System

1 cubic centimeter (cc or cm³) = 1000 cubic millimeters (cu mm or mm³)

1 cubic decimeter (cu dm or dm³) = 1000 cc

1 cubic meter (cu m or m³) = 1000 cu dm

1 liter (l) = 1 cu dm = 1000 cc

CAPACITY

Liquid Measure	*Dry Measure*
1 fluid drachm (f ʒ) = 60 minims	1 quart (qt) = 2 pints (pt)
1 fluid ounce (f ℥) = 8 f ʒ	1 small measure = 2 qt
1 pint (pt) = 16 f ℥	1 peck (pk) = 8 qt
= 4 gills	1 bushel (bu) = 4 pk
1 quart (qt) = 2 pt	
1 gallon (gal) = 4 qt	
1 barrel (bbl) = 31½ gal	
1 hogshead (hhd) = 2 bbl	

Approximate Equivalents

1 bu (stroked) contains 2150.4 cu in.	1 teaspoonful = 4 cc
1 bu (stroked) contains 1¼ cu ft	1 dessertspoonful = 8 cc
1 cu ft = 0.8 bu	1 tablespoonful = 15 cc
1 cu ft contains 7½ gal	1 fluid ounce = 2 tablespoons
1 dry quart contains 67⅕ cu in.	1 cup = 120 cc
1 liquid quart contains 57¾ cu in.	1 pt = 2 cups
1 gal. contains 231 cu in.	= 24 tablespoons
1 gal = 3.785 liters	

Table I. Measurements (Cont.)

WEIGHT

Avoirdupois

1 ounce (oz) = 437½ grains
1 pound (lb) = 16 oz
1 hundredweight (cwt) = 100 lb
1 short ton = 2000 lb
1 long ton = 2240 lb

Apothecaries'

1 scruple (℈) = 20 grains
1 drachm (ʒ) = 3℈
1 ounce (℥) = 12ʒ
1 pound (lb) = 8℥

Metric

1 gram (g) = weight of 1 cc of water at 4° C
1 milligram (mg) = 0.001 g
1 centigram (cg) = 0.01 g
1 decigram (dg) = 0.1 g
1 kilogram (kg) = 1000 g
1 metric ton = 1,000,000 g

Approximate Equivalents

1 avoirdupois grain = 1 apothecaries' grain
1 g = 0.03527 oz
1 g = 15.4324 grains
1 oz = 28.35 g
1 lb = 453.59 g
1 kilogram = 2.2 lb
1 cu ft of water weighs 62½ lb

TIME

1 minute (min) = 60 sec
1 hour (hr) = 60 min
1 day = 24 hr
1 week = 7 days
1 month = 30 days (nominally, for ordinary
accounting)
1 year (yr) = 12 months
= 52 weeks (nearly)
= 365 days
1 leap year = 366 days
1 decade = 10 yr
1 century = 100 yr

TEMPERATURE

A change of 1° centigrade (C) is equivalent to a change of 1.8° Fahrenheit (F).
A change of 1° F is equivalent to a change of $\frac{5}{9}$ of 1° C.
Water freezes at 0° C, or 32° F.
Water boils at 100° C, or 212° F.

182

TABLES

Table I. Measurements (Cont.)

HEAT, ENERGY, WORK, AND POWER

1 small calorie = amount of heat required to raise 1 g of water 1° C
1 large calorie = 1000 small calories
1 therm = 1000 large calories
1 foot-pound (ft-lb) = work done by force of 1 lb acting through a distance of 1 ft
Power = rate of doing work
1 horsepower (hp) = 550 ft-lb per second
= 746 watts (w)
1 kilowatt (kw) = 1000 w
1 kilowatt-hour (kwhr) = energy produced by 1 kw of power acting for 1 hr

COUNTING

1 dozen (doz) = 12 units
1 gross = 12 doz
1 great gross = 12 gross
1 score = 20 units

ANGLES

1 minute (') = 60 seconds (")
1 degree (°) = 60'
1 radian = 57.3° (nearly)
1 right angle ($\llcorner$) = 90°
= $\pi/2$ radians
1 straight angle (st. $\angle$) = 180°
= π radians
1 revolution (rev) = 360°
= 2π radians
π = 3.1416 or $3\frac{1}{7}$, approx.

Table II. Convenient Equivalents*

CONSTRUCTION MATERIALS

Brick

1 brick is considered as measuring 2 in. × 4 in. × 8 in.
1 cu ft brick work contains 22 bricks.
1 cu ft brick weighs 125 lb.

Concrete

1 bag cement occupies 0.94 cu ft.
1 bag cement weighs 94 lb.
1 bbl cement contains 4 bags.
1 bbl cement occupies 3.76 cu ft.
1 bbl cement weighs 376 lb.

1 cu ft cement weighs 100 lb.
1 cu ft concrete weighs 140 lb.
1 cu ft crushed stone weighs 100 lb.
1 cu ft sand weighs 105 lb.

* Many of these equivalents are approximations.

Table II. Convenient Equivalents (Cont.)

CONSTRUCTION MATERIALS (Cont.)

Iron

1 cu ft cast iron weighs 450 lb.
1 cu ft wrought iron weighs 480 lb.
1 cu ft steel weighs 490 lb.
1 lb size 6d common nails = 168 nails.
1 lb size 8d common nails = 106 nails.
1 lb size 16d common nails = 49 nails.
1 lb size 20d common nails = 31 nails.

Lumber

1 cu ft red oak weighs 45 lb.
1 cu ft white oak weighs 46 lb.
1 cu ft white pine weighs 27 lb.
1 cu ft yellow pine weighs 41 lb.
1 board foot (bd ft) is the equivalent of a piece of lumber 1 ft square and 1 in. (or less) thick.
1 sq ft of roof requires ten 4-in. shingles.
1 square of roofing covers 100 sq ft.

Paint

1 gal paint covers 300 sq ft, two coats.

PRODUCE

1 bu grain occupies $1\frac{1}{4}$ cu ft.
1 bu ear corn, without husk, occupies $2\frac{1}{2}$ cu ft.
1 bu ear corn, with husk, occupies $3\frac{1}{2}$ cu ft.
1 ton hay occupies 500 cu ft.
1 ton silage occupies 50 cu ft.
1 gal 20% cream weighs 8.4 lb.
1 gal 22% cream weighs 8.339 lb.
1 gal skim milk weighs 8.65 lb.
1 gal 3% milk weighs 8.60 lb.
1 gal average milk weighs 8.6 lb.
1 gal 4% milk weighs 8.59 lb.
1 gal 5% milk weighs 8.58 lb.
1 gal water weighs 8.339 lb.
1 lb whole eggs = 8 to 10 eggs.
1 case of eggs = 30 doz. eggs
1 cu ft soft coal weighs 50 lb.
1 cu ft hard coal weighs 56 lb.
1 cu ft limestone weighs 164 lb.

Table III. Weights of Commodities per Bushel*

Commodity	Weight (lb)	Commodity	Weight (lb)
Alfalfa seed	60	Milo maize	50
Apples	48	Oats	32
Barley	48	Onions	57
Beans, snap	30	Peaches	50
Beans, dry	60	Peanuts, roasted	20
Beans, castor	46	Peanuts, Spanish	24
Bran	20	Pears	58
Buckwheat	52	Peas, dried	60
Clover seed	60	Peas, green, in pod	32
Coal, anthracite	80	Plums	56
Broom-corn seed	48	Prunes	56
Cherries, with stems	56	Popcorn, ear	70
Clover seed	60	Popcorn, shelled	56
Corn meal, unbolted	50	Potatoes, Irish	60
Corn, ear, new crop before Dec. 1	72	Potatoes, sweet	50
		Rye	56
Corn, ear, after Dec 1	70	Salt, coarse	55
Corn (green, sweet)	35	Salt, fine	50
Corn, shelled	56	Shorts	20
Cottonseed	32	Sorghum seed	50
Cowpeas	60	Soybeans	60
Cranberries	33	Spinach	18
Cucumbers	48	Sudan grass seed	40
Flaxseed	56	Timothy seed	45
Grapes	48	Tomatoes	56
Kafir	50	Turnips	55
Millet	50	Wheat	60

* There is some variation in legal weights of certain commodities per bushel in different states.

Table IV. Proportions of Cement, Sand, and Gravel in Concrete Mixtures

Description of Mixture	Use	Proportion
Rich	Structural parts under heavy stress, and watertight structures	1–1½–3
Standard	Reinforced concrete under considerable stress (floors, beams, and columns)	1–2–4
Medium	Plain concrete of moderate strength (walls and sidewalks)	1–2½–5
Lean	Concrete under compression only	1–3–6

Table V. Approximate Number of Board Feet of Lumber in Trees Containing One, Two, or Three 16-ft Merchantable Logs*

Diameter of Tree at 4½ ft Above Ground (in.)	Board Feet in Tree Having One 16-ft Log	Board Feet in Tree Having Two 16-ft Logs	Board Feet in Tree Having Three 16-ft Logs
8	19	32	—
9	27	43	—
10	36	57	64
11	46	73	84
12	58	90	108
13	68	110	131
14	80	130	160
15	92	154	192
16	106	181	226
17	120	208	260
18	136	234	305
19	150	263	350
20	169	300	396
21	180	335	440
22	204	365	485
23	225	395	530
24	246	430	580

* This table was made primarily for use on Southern pine trees, but it may be used in estimating the board-foot content of straight trunks and limbs of other kinds of trees.

Table VI. Per Cent of Nitrogen, Phosphoric Acid, and Potash in Common Fertilizer Materials

Type of Material	Fertilizing Material	Nitrogen (%)	Available Phosphoric Acid (%)	Potash (%)
Nitrogenous	Cyanamid	21	0	0
	Dried blood	13	0	0
	Sodium nitrate	16	0	0
	Ammonium sulfate	20	0	0
Phosphatic	Acid phosphate	0	16	0
	Basic slag	0	15	0
	Phosphate of lime	0	12	0
	Superphosphate (18%)	0	18	0
	Superphosphate (20%)	0	20	0
	Superphosphate (32%)	0	32	0
	Superphosphate (45%)	0	45	0
Potash	Muriate of potash	0	0	50
	Kainit	0	0	12
	Sulfate of Potash	0	0	48
Combined nitrogenous and phosphatic	Bone meal	4	23	0
	Ground tankage	8	10	0
	Fish scrap	8	7	0
Combined phosphatic and potash	Wood ashes	0	1	6
Combined nitrogenous, phosphatic, and potash	Cottonseed	3.13	1.27	1.17
	Cottonseed meal	7	2.5	1.5
	Farmyard manure	0.5	0.5	0.5
	Hen manure (dry)	2	2	1
	Pea straw	0.1	0.3	1
	Leaves	0.7	0.15	0.3

Table VII. Plant Food Nutrient Content of Crops

Crop	Yield	Nitrogen (lb)	Phosphoric Acid (lb)	Potash
Alfalfa	3 tons	140	35	135
Barley				
grain..................	40 bu	35	15	10
straw	1 ton	15	5	30
Cabbage	15 tons	100	25	100
Celery	350 crates	80	65	235
Corn				
grain..................	60 bu	57	23	15
stover................	2 tons	38	12	55
Cotton				
lint	500 lb			
seed..................	1000 lb	38	18	14
burrs, leaves, stalks	1500 lb	27	7	36
Cow Peas	2 tons	125	25	90
Lespedeza	3 tons	130	30	70
Oats				
grain.................	50 bu	35	15	10
straw	1.25 tons	15	5	35
Pea Beans				
beans	30 bu	73	23	24
straw		22	7	31
Peanuts				
nuts	1 ton	60	10	10
vines.................	3 tons	25	5	40
Potatoes				
tubers................	300 bu	65	25	115
tops..................		60	10	55
Soybeans				
beans.	25 bu	110	35	40
straw	1.25 tons	15	5	20
Spinach	9 tons	90	30	45
Sugar Beets				
roots	15 tons	55	22	53
tops..................		60	23	92
Sweet Potatoes				
roots	300 bu	45	15	75
vines.................		30	5	40
Tobacco				
leaves	1500 lb	55	10	80
stalks		25	10	35
Tomatoes				
fruit	10 tons	60	20	80
vines.................		40	15	95
Wheat				
grain.................	30 bu	35	16	9
straw	1.25 tons	15	4	21

Table VIII. Average Percentage Composition of Feeds

first 4 Considered
as nutrients of feed

Feeds	Pro-tein	Ether Ex-tract	Crude Fiber	Nitro-gen-Free Ex-tract	Water	Ash	Digest-ible Pro-tein
Alfalfa hay	14.8	2.0	29.1	37.4	8.3	8.4	11.0
Alfalfa leaf meal	21.5	2.6	15.8	40.5	7.7	11.9	16.1
Alfalfa meal	14.6	1.8	29.9	36.8	8.6	8.3	10.9
Barley chops (grain)	12.0	2.1	6.3	67.5	9.3	2.8	9.6
Beet pulp, dried	9.0	0.6	19.3	59.0	8.5	3.6	4.5
Bermuda hay	5.9	1.5	26.7	50.3	7.8	7.8	3.0
Bone meal, raw	25.5	2.2	1.2	4.2	5.2	61.7	21.2
Buttermilk, dried	34.4	5.0	0.4	40.6	8.2	11.4	32.6
Cod liver oil	52.1	27.1	0.9	10.1	7.0	2.8	43.2
Corn, grain	10.4	4.4	2.3	72.5	9.1	1.3	6.4
Corn cob	3.1	0.5	33.0	54.0	7.3	2.1	0.3
Corn feed meal	9.9	4.4	3.0	70.3	10.7	1.7	6.4
Corn meal	10.1	3.5	1.7	73.1	10.4	1.2	6.5
Cottonseed	20.9	17.9	23.8	26.9	7.0	3.5	15.4
Cottonseed cake	43.0	6.0	12.0	23.0	—	—	34.5
Cottonseed meal	43.0	6.0	12.0	23.0	—	—	35.7
Cottonseed hulls	4.1	0.9	47.6	35.3	9.4	2.7	0.4
Cowpea hay	13.1	2.9	30.6	33.9	9.6	9.9	9.0
Feterita heads	10.6	2.7	7.4	65.9	10.2	3.2	8.1
Hegari, grain or chops	11.4	2.1	2.4	70.8	11.8	1.5	8.8
Johnson grass hay	6.1	1.7	29.1	45.6	7.4	10.1	2.7
Kafir grain or chops	11.2	2.9	2.3	71.1	10.5	2.0	8.6
Linseed meal	32.2	10.2	9.9	37.6	5.3	4.8	27.0
Meat scraps	61.2	11.8	3.2	1.7	6.2	15.9	60.5
Milk, dried, skimmed	35.6	0.3	0.1	51.3	5.1	7.6	33.5
Milo heads	10.1	2.5	6.8	67.1	10.0	3.5	7.6
Molasses, blackstrap	2.4	0.0	0.0	65.0	—	—	0.3
Oats, whole ground	12.2	4.6	11.4	58.9	9.1	3.8	9.6
Oatmeal	14.9	5.4	3.5	65.8	8.2	2.2	13.4
Peanut hay	10.0	3.5	24.0	44.0	—	—	—
Rice, ground whole	7.6	1.9	9.2	64.8	11.5	5.0	5.8
Rice bran	12.8	13.1	12.7	41.7	9.0	10.7	8.9
Sorghum hay or fodder	5.7	2.2	19.0	48.5	18.6	6.0	1.8
Sorghum and corn silage	4.9	1.6	13.0	36.8	39.6	4.1	0.8
Soybean oil meal	44.6	7.2	5.1	29.2	7.9	6.0	37.2
Sudan grass hay	8.6	1.8	29.7	43.4	8.4	8.1	4.5
Tankage	48.6	9.7	2.8	2.9	6.7	29.3	33.8
Wheat	14.0	1.7	3.0	69.4	10.0	1.9	11.3
Wheat bran	16.9	4.0	8.8	54.9	9.7	5.7	13.3
Wheat gray shorts	18.0	4.5	5.6	57.8	10.0	4.1	14.9

Protean 3 5 lb × .11lb / 1lb = 3 85 lb

Table IX. Number of Pounds of Digestible Nutrients in 100 lb. of Feed*

Feed	Protein	Ether Extract	Crude Fiber	Nitrogen-Free Extract	Total**	Productive Energy per 100 lb (therms)
Alfalfa hay............	11.0	0.7	13.0	26.5	52.1	37.4
Alfalfa leaf meal	16.1	0.8	8.7	32.4	59.0	52.3
Alfalfa meal	10.9	0.5	14.0	26.0	52.0	41.2
Barley (grain)	9.6	1.8	4.4	62.7	80.7	74.4
Beet pulp, dried.......	4.5	0	16.2	49.0	69.7	75.1
Bermuda hay.........	3.0	0.7	14.3	26.0	44.9	31.3
Corn, grain...........	6.4	3.8	0.7	66.7	82.3	84.8
Corn cob.............	0.3	0.1	18.1	26.4	45.0	13.6
Corn meal............	6.5	3.3	1.0	68.6	83.5	86.8
Cottonseed	15.4	15.6	18.0	13.2	81.7	76.6
Cottonseed meal	35.7	7.2	3.9	17.8	73.8	74.9
Cottonseed hulls	0.4	0.7	23.2	18.5	43.7	17.9
Cowpea hay	9.0	1.2	14.3	23.1	49.1	32.6
Kafir grain or chops ...	8.6	2.2	0.6	63.1	77.2	85.8
Linseed meal	27.0	9.4	5.9	30.8	84.8	85.0
Milk, dried, skimmed ..	33.5	0.3	0.1	50.3	84.6	85.8
Milo heads	7.6	2.2	3.5	60.9	76.9	77.5
Molasses, blackstrap...	0.3	0	0	57.6	57.9	62.8
Oats, whole ground....	9.6	3.9	4.7	48.3	81.4	71.9
Peanut hay	6.5	2.1	12.2	33.3	56.7	45.2
Rice, ground whole	5.8	1.4	1.0	58.8	69.7	70.2
Rice bran	8.9	10.8	2.9	31.5	67.6	69.9
Sorghum hay or fodder.	1.8	1.3	11.5	28.6	44.8	35.7
Sorghum and corn silage	0.8	0.9	6.4	24.2	33.4	28.6
Sudan grass hay.......	4.5	0.8	19.3	23.7	49.3	33.9
Tankage	33.8	8.8	2.0	2.2	57.8	59.7
Wheat...............	11.3	1.3	1.8	65.2	81.2	78.8
Wheat bran	13.3	2.7	2.8	39.5	61.7	56.8
Wheat gray shorts.....	14.9	4.0	2.0	52.2	78.1	75.7

* Computed from data given in Bulletins 329, 402, 454, and 461 of the Texas Agricultural Experiment Station.

** Totals include 2.25 times digestible ether extracts.

Table X. Tentative Standards for Feeding per Day per 1000 lb Live Weight*

Animal	Per day per 1000 lb Live Weight		
	Dry Matter (lb)	Digestible Crude Protein (lb)	Productive Value (therms)
Growing dairy cattle:			
Weight 100–200 lb	22.0–24.0	2.8–3.1	15.6–17.5
Weight 200–300 lb	23.0–25.0	2.5–2.8	15.1–17.0
Weight 300–400 lb	24.0–26.0	2.2–2.5	14.2–16.0
Weight 400–500 lb	22.0–25.0	1.9–2.2	13.3–15.0
Weight 500–600 lb	21.5–24.5	1.7–1.9	12.6–14.5
Weight 600–700 lb	21.0–24.0	1.6–1.8	12.0–13.8
Weight 700–800 lb	20.5–23.5	1.5–1.7	11.0–13.0
Weight 800–900 lb	20.0–23.0	1.4–1.6	10.4–12.3
Weight 900–1000 lb	20.0–23.0	1.2–1.9	9.7–11.4
Growing steers with some fattening:			
Weight 100–200 lb	22.0–24.0	2.8–3.1	15.8–17.7
Weight 200–300 lb	23.0–25.0	2.5–2.8	15.6–17.5
Weight 300–400 lb	24.0–26.0	2.2–2.5	14.5–16.4
Weight 400–500 lb	24.0–26.0	2.0–2.2	14.0–15.9
Weight 500–600 lb	23.0–25.0	1.9–2.1	13.7–15.5
Weight 600–700 lb	22.0–24.0	1.8–2.0	13.3–15.2
Weight 700–800 lb	21.0–23.0	1.7–1.9	13.0–14.9
Weight 800–900 lb	20.5–22.5	1.6–1.8	12.6–14.5
Weight 900–1000 lb	20.0–22.0	1.5–1.7	12.3–14.1
Weight 1000–1100 lb	19.5–21.5	1.4–1.6	11.8–13.7
Weight 1100–1200 lb	19.0–21.0	1.3–1.5	11.4–13.3
Fattening 2-yr-old steers on full feed:			
First 40–60 days	22.0–28.0	1.7–2.0	14.3–16.2
Second 40–60 days	20.0–30.0	1.6–1.9	13.2–15.7
Third 40–60 days	18.0–28.0	1.5–1.8	13.0–15.3
Ox at rest in stall	13.0–21.0	0.5–0.7	6.8–7.8
Wintering beef cows and calves	14.0–25.0	0.7–0.8	8.0–10.0
Horses:			
Idle	13.0–19.0	0.8–1.0	6.5–8.4
At light work	15.0–21.0	1.0–1.2	8.4–10.5
At medium work	16.0–22.0	1.2–1.5	10.0–13.0
At heavy work	18.0–24.0	1.5–2.0	13.0–16.0

* Standards taken from Bulletins 454 and 461 of the Texas Agricultural Experiment Station.

Table X
Tentative Standards for Feeding per Day per 1000 lb. Live Weight (Cont.)

Animal	Per Day per 1000 lb Live Weight		
	Dry Matter (lb)	Digestible Crude Protein (lb)	Productive Value (therms)
Brood mares suckling foals, but not at work..	15.0–22.0	1.2–1.4	8.4–11.2
Growing colts, over 6 months..............	18.0–22.0	1.6–1.8	10.0–12.0
Fattening lambs:			
Weight 50–70 lb	27.0–30.0	2.6–3.0	18.0–20.5
Weight 70–90 lb	28.0–31.0	2.4–2.7	18.0–21.4
Weight 90–100 lb	27.0–31.0	2.2–2.4	18.0–21.4
Fattening sheep	24.0–32.0	1.6–2.0	15.0–16.0
Dairy cows:			
For maintenance of 1000-lb cow		0.60	6.0
To allowance for maintenance add:			
For each pound of 3.0% milk........		0.045–0.055	0.25
For each pound of 4.0% milk........		0.053–0.065	0.30
For each pound of 5.0% milk........		0.060–0.070	0.35
For each pound of 6.0% milk........		0.065–0.080	0.40
For each pound of 7.0% milk........		0.070–0.085	0.45
Sheep maintaining, mature:			
Coarse wool.........................	18.0–23.0	1.0–1.3	9.5–12.0
Fine wool	20.0–26.0	1.1–1.4	10.5–13.0
Breeding ewes, with lambs	23.0–27.0	2.5–2.8	16.7–18.6
Fattening hogs:			
Weight 30–50 lb	44.0–63.0	7.0–8.0	35.0–50.0
Weight 50–100 lb	33.0–43.0	5.3–6.0	30.0–34.0
Weight 100–150 lb	30.0–41.0	4.4–5.0	26.0–33.0
Weight 150–200 lb	28.0–38.0	3.4–4.2	24.0–31.0
Weight 200–250 lb	25.0–36.0	2.9–3.8	21.0–29.0
Weight 250–300 lb	20.0–32.0	2.6–3.4	18.0–26.0
Brood sows with pigs....................	20.0–28.0	2.4–3.0	16.0–24.0

Table XI. Trigonometric Functions*

Angle	Sine	Tangent	Cotangent	Cosine	
0° 00′	.0000	.0000	——	1.0000	90° 00′
10	.0029	.0029	343.77	1.0000	50
20	.0058	.0058	171.89	1.0000	40
30	.0087	.0087	114.59	1.0000	30
40	.0116	.0116	85.940	.9999	20
50	.0145	.0145	68.750	.9999	10
1° 00′	.0175	.0175	57.290	.9998	89° 00′
10	.0204	.0204	49.104	.9998	50
20	.0233	.0233	42.964	.9997	40
30	.0262	.0262	38.188	.9997	30
40	.0291	.0291	34.368	.9996	20
50	.0320	.0320	31.242	.9995	10
2° 00′	.0349	.0349	28.636	.9994	88° 00′
10	.0378	.0378	26.432	.9993	50
20	.0407	.0407	24.542	.9992	40
30	.0436	.0437	22.904	.9990	30
40	.0465	.0466	21.470	.9989	20
50	.0494	.0495	20.206	.9988	10
3° 00′	.0523	.0524	19.081	.9986	87° 00′
10	.0552	.0553	18.075	.9985	50
20	.0581	.0582	17.169	.9983	40
30	.0610	.0612	16.350	.9981	30
40	.0640	.0641	15.605	.9980	20
50	.0669	.0670	14.924	.9978	10
4° 00′	.0698	.0699	14.301	.9976	86° 00′
10	.0727	.0729	13.727	.9974	50
20	.0756	.0758	13.197	.9971	40
30	.0785	.0787	12.706	.9969	30
40	.0814	.0816	12.251	.9967	20
50	.0843	.0846	11.826	.9964	10
5° 00′	.0872	.0875	11.430	.9962	85° 00′
	Cosine	Cotangent	Tangent	Sine	Angle

* Adapted from W. W. Elliott and Edward R. C. Miles, *College Mathematics: A First Course*, 2nd Ed. New York: Prentice-Hall, Inc., 1951.

Table XI. Trigonometric Functions (Cont.)

Angle	Sine	Tan-gent	Cotan-gent	Cosine	
5° 00′	.0872	.0875	11.430	.9962	**85° 00′**
10	.0901	.0904	11.059	.9959	50
20	.0929	.0934	10.712	.9957	40
30	.0958	.0963	10.385	.9954	**30**
40	.0987	.0992	10.078	.9951	20
50	.1016	.1022	9.7882	.9948	10
6° 00′	.1045	.1051	9.5144	.9945	**84° 00′**
10	.1074	.1080	9.2553	.9942	50
20	.1103	.1110	9.0098	.9939	40
30	.1132	.1139	8.7769	.9936	**30**
40	.1161	.1169	8.5555	.9932	20
50	.1190	.1198	8.3450	.9929	10
7° 00′	.1219	.1228	8.1443	.9925	**83° 00′**
10	.1248	.1257	7.9530	.9922	50
20	.1276	.1287	7.7704	.9918	40
30	.1305	.1317	7.5958	.9914	**30**
40	.1334	.1346	7.4287	.9911	20
50	.1363	.1376	7.2687	.9907	10
8° 00′	.1392	.1405	7.1154	.9903	**82° 00′**
10	.1421	.1435	6.9682	.9899	50
20	.1449	.1465	6.8269	.9894	40
30	.1478	.1495	6.6912	.9890	**30**
40	.1507	.1524	6.5606	.9886	20
50	.1536	.1554	6.4348	.9881	10
9° 00′	.1564	.1584	6.3138	.9877	**81° 00′**
10	.1593	.1614	6.1970	.9872	50
20	.1622	.1644	6.0844	.9868	40
30	.1650	.1673	5.9758	.9863	**30**
40	.1679	.1703	5.8708	.9858	20
50	.1708	.1733	5.7694	.9853	10
10° 00′	.1736	.1763	5.6713	.9848	**80° 00′**
	Cosine	Cotan-gent	Tan-gent	Sine	Angle

Table XI. Trigonometric Functions (Cont.)

Angle	Sine	Tan-gent	Cotan-gent	Cosine	
10° 00′	.1736	.1763	5.6713	.9848	80° 00′
10	.1765	.1793	5.5764	.9843	50
20	.1794	.1823	5.4845	.9838	40
30	.1822	.1853	5.3955	.9833	30
40	.1851	.1883	5.3093	.9827	20
50	.1880	.1914	5.2257	.9822	10
11° 00′	.1908	.1944	5.1446	.9816	79° 00′
10	.1937	.1974	5.0658	.9811	50
20	.1965	.2004	4.9894	.9805	40
30	.1994	.2035	4.9152	.9799	30
40	.2022	.2065	4.8430	.9793	20
50	.2051	.2095	4.7729	.9787	10
12° 00′	.2079	.2126	4.7046	.9781	78° 00′
10	.2108	.2156	4.6382	.9775	50
20	.2136	.2186	4.5736	.9769	40
30	.2164	.2217	4.5107	.9763	30
40	.2193	.2247	4.4494	.9757	20
50	.2221	.2278	4.3897	.9750	10
13° 00′	.2250	.2309	4.3315	.9744	77° 00′
10	.2278	.2339	4.2747	.9737	50
20	.2306	.2370	4.2193	.9730	40
30	.2334	.2401	4.1653	.9724	30
40	.2363	.2432	4.1126	.9717	20
50	.2391	.2462	4.0611	.9710	10
14° 00′	.2419	.2493	4.0108	.9703	76° 00′
10	.2447	.2524	3.9617	.9696	50
20	.2476	.2555	3.9136	.9689	40
30	.2504	.2586	3.8667	.9681	30
40	.2532	.2617	3.8208	.9674	20
50	.2560	.2648	3.7760	.9667	10
15° 00′	.2588	.2679	3.7321	.9659	75° 00′
	Cosine	Cotan-gent	Tan-gent	Sine	Angle

Table XI. Trigonometric Functions (Cont.)

Angle	Sine	Tangent	Cotangent	Cosine	
15° 00′	.2588	.2679	3.7321	.9659	**75° 00′**
10	.2616	.2711	3.6891	.9652	50
20	.2644	.2742	3.6470	.9644	40
30	.2672	.2773	3.6059	.9636	**30**
40	.2700	.2805	3.5656	.9628	20
50	.2728	.2836	3.5261	.9621	10
16° 00′	.2756	.2867	3.4874	.9613	**74° 00′**
10	.2784	.2899	3.4495	.9605	50
20	.2812	.2931	3.4124	.9596	40
30	.2840	.2962	3.3759	.9588	**30**
40	.2868	.2994	3.3402	.9580	20
50	.2896	.3026	3.3052	.9572	10
17° 00′	.2924	.3057	3.2709	.9563	**73° 00′**
10	.2952	.3089	3.2371	.9555	50
20	.2979	.3121	3.2041	.9546	40
30	.3007	.3153	3.1716	.9537	**30**
40	.3035	.3185	3.1397	.9528	20
50	.3062	.3217	3.1084	.9520	10
18° 00′	.3090	.3249	3.0777	.9511	**72° 00′**
10	.3118	.3281	3.0475	.9502	50
20	.3145	.3314	3.0178	.9492	40
30	.3173	.3346	2.9887	.9483	**30**
40	.3201	.3378	2.9600	.9474	20
50	.3228	.3411	2.9319	.9465	10
19° 00′	.3256	.3443	2.9042	.9455	**71° 00′**
10	.3283	.3476	2.8770	.9446	50
20	.3311	.3508	2.8502	.9436	40
30	.3338	.3541	2.8239	.9426	**30**
40	.3365	.3574	2.7980	.9417	20
50	.3393	.3607	2.7725	.9407	10
20° 00′	.3420	.3640	2.7475	.9397	**70° 00′**
	Cosine	Cotangent	Tangent	Sine	Angle

TABLES

Table XI. Trigonometric Functions (Cont.)

Angle	Sine	Tangent	Cotangent	Cosine	
20° 00'	.3420	.3640	2.7475	.9397	**70° 00'**
10	.3448	.3673	2.7228	.9387	50
20	.3475	.3706	2.6985	.9377	40
30	.3502	.3739	2.6746	.9367	**30**
40	.3529	.3772	2.6511	.9356	20
50	.3557	.3805	2.6279	.9346	10
21° 00'	.3584	.3839	2.6051	.9336	**69° 00'**
10	.3611	.3872	2.5826	.9325	50
20	.3638	.3906	2.5605	.9315	40
30	.3665	.3939	2.5386	.9304	**30**
40	.3692	.3973	2.5172	.9293	20
50	.3719	.4006	2.4960	.9283	10
22° 00'	.3746	.4040	2.4751	.9272	**68° 00'**
10	.3773	.4074	2.4545	.9261	50
20	.3800	.4108	2.4342	.9250	40
30	.3827	.4142	2.4142	.9239	**30**
40	.3854	.4176	2.3945	.9228	20
50	.3881	.4210	2.3750	.9216	10
23° 00'	.2907	.4245	2.3559	.9205	**67° 00'**
10	.3934	.4279	2.3369	.9194	50
20	.3961	.4314	2.3183	.9182	04
30	.3987	.4348	2.2998	.9171	**30**
40	.4014	.4383	2.2817	.9159	20
50	.4041	.4417	2.2637	.9147	10
24° 00'	.4067	.4452	2.2460	.9135	**66° 00'**
10	.4094	.4487	2.2286	.9124	50
20	.4120	.4522	2.2113	.9112	40
30	.4147	.4557	2.1943	.9100	**30**
40	.4173	.4592	2.1775	.9088	20
50	.4200	.4628	2.1609	.9075	10
25° 00'	.4226	.4663	2.1445	.9063	**65° 00'**
	Cosine	Cotangent	Tangent	Sine	Angle

Table XI. Trigonometric Functions (Cont.)

Angle	Sine	Tan-gent	Cotan-gent	Cosine	
25° 00'	.4226	.4663	2.1445	.9063	**65° 00'**
10	.4253	.4699	2.1283	.9051	50
20	.4279	.4734	2.1123	.9038	40
30	.4305	.4770	2.0965	.9026	**30**
40	.4331	.4806	2.0809	.9013	20
50	.4358	.4841	2.0655	.9001	10
26° 00'	.4384	.4877	2.0503	.8988	**64° 00'**
10	.4410	.4913	2.0353	.8975	50
20	.4436	.4950	2.0204	.8962	40
30	.4462	.4986	2.0057	.8949	**30**
40	.4488	.5022	1.9912	.8936	20
50	.4514	.5059	1.9768	.8923	10
27° 00'	.4540	.5095	1.9626	.8910	**63° 00'**
10	.4566	.5132	1.9486	.8897	50
20	.4592	.5169	1.9347	.8884	40
30	.4617	.5206	1.9210	.8870	**30**
40	.4643	.5243	1.9074	.8857	20
50	.4669	.5280	1.8940	.8843	10
28° 00'	.4695	.5317	1.8807	.8829	**62° 00'**
10	.4720	.5354	1.8676	.8816	50
20	.4746	.5392	1.8546	.8802	40
30	.4772	.5430	1.8418	.8788	**30**
40	.4797	.5467	1.8291	.8774	20
50	.4823	.5505	1.8165	.8760	10
29° 00'	.4848	.5543	1.8040	.8746	**61° 00'**
10	.4874	.5581	1.7917	.8732	50
20	.4899	.5619	1.7796	.8718	40
30	.4924	.5658	1.7675	.8704	**30**
40	.4950	.5696	1.7556	.8689	20
50	.4975	.5735	1.7437	.8675	10
30° 00'	.5000	.5774	1.7321	.8660	**60° 00'**
	Cosine	Cotan-gent	Tan-gent	Sine	Angle

TABLES

Table XI. Trigonometric Functions (Cont.)

Angle	Sine	Tangent	Cotangent	Cosine	
30° 00′	.5000	.5774	1.7321	.8660	**60° 00′**
10	.5025	.5812	1.7205	.8646	50
20	.5050	.5851	1.7090	.8631	40
30	.5075	.5890	1.6977	.8616	**30**
40	.5100	.5930	1.6864	.8601	20
50	.5125	.5969	1.6753	.8587	10
31° 00′	.5150	.6009	1.6643	.8572	**59° 00′**
10	.5175	.6048	1.6534	.8557	50
20	.5200	.6088	1.6426	.8542	40
30	.5225	.6128	1.6319	.8526	**30**
40	.5250	.6168	1.6212	.8511	20
50	.5275	.6208	1.6107	.8496	10
32° 00′	.5299	.6249	1.6003	.8480	**58° 00′**
10	.5324	.6289	1.5900	.8465	50
20	.5348	.6330	1.5798	.8450	40
30	.5373	.6371	1.5697	.8434	**30**
40	.5398	.6412	1.5597	.8418	20
50	.5422	.6453	1.5497	.8403	10
33° 00′	.5446	.6494	1.5399	.8387	**57° 00′**
10	.5471	.6536	1.5301	.8371	50
20	.5495	.6577	1.5204	.8355	40
30	.5519	.6619	1.5108	.8339	**30**
40	.5544	.6661	1.5013	.8323	20
50	.5568	.6703	1.4919	.8307	10
34° 00′	.5592	.6745	1.4826	.8290	**56° 00′**
10	.5616	.6787	1.4733	.8274	50
20	.5640	.6830	1.4641	.8258	40
30	.5664	.6873	1.4550	.8241	**30**
40	.5688	.6916	1.4460	.8225	20
50	.5712	.6959	1.4370	.8208	10
35° 00′	.5736	.7002	1.4281	.8192	**55° 00′**
	Cosine	Cotangent	Tangent	Sine	Angle

Table XI. Trigonometric Functions (Cont.)

Angle	Sine	Tangent	Cotangent	Cosine	
35° 00′	.5736	.7002	1.4281	.8192	**55° 00′**
10	.5760	.7046	1.4193	.8175	50
20	.5783	.7089	1.4106	.8158	40
30	.5807	.7133	1.4019	.8141	**30**
40	.5831	.7177	1.3934	.8124	20
50	.5854	.7221	1.3848	.8107	10
36° 00′	.5878	.7265	1.3764	.8090	**54° 00′**
10	.5901	.7310	1.3680	.8073	50
20	.5925	.7355	1.3597	.8056	40
30	.5948	.7400	1.3514	.8039	**30**
40	.5972	.7445	1.3432	.8021	20
50	.5995	.7490	1.3351	.8004	10
37° 00′	.6018	.7536	1.3270	.7986	**53° 00′**
10	.6041	.7581	1.3190	.7969	50
20	.6065	.7627	1.3111	.7951	40
30	.6088	.7673	1.3032	.7934	**30**
40	.6111	.7720	1.2954	.7916	20
50	.6134	.7766	1.2876	.7898	10
38° 00′	.6157	.7813	1.2799	.7880	**52° 00′**
10	.6180	.7860	1.2723	.7862	50
20	.6202	.7907	1.2647	.7844	40
30	.6225	.7954	1.2572	.7826	**30**
40	.6248	.8002	1.2497	.7808	20
50	.6271	.8050	1.2423	.7790	10
39° 00′	.6293	.8098	1.2349	.7771	**51° 00′**
10	.6316	.8146	1.2276	.7753	50
20	.6338	.8195	1.2203	.7735	40
30	.6361	.8243	1.2131	.7716	**30**
40	.6383	.8292	1.2059	.7698	20
50	.6406	.8342	1.1988	.7679	10
40° 00′	.6428	.8391	1.1918	.7660	**50° 00′**
	Cosine	Cotangent	Tangent	Sine	Angle

Table XI. Trigonometric Functions (Cont.)

Angle	Sine	Tan-gent	Cotan-gent	Cosine	
40° 00′	.6428	.8391	1.1918	.7660	50° 00′
10	.6450	.8441	1.1847	.7642	50
20	.6472	.8491	1.1778	.7623	40
30	.6494	.8541	1.1708	.7604	30
40	.6517	.8591	1.1640	.7585	20
50	.6539	.8642	1.1571	.7566	10
41° 00′	.6561	.8693	1.1504	.7547	49° 00′
10	.6583	.8744	1.1436	.7528	50
20	.6604	.8796	1.1369	.7509	40
30	.6626	.8847	1.1303	.7490	30
40	.6648	.8899	1.1237	.7470	20
50	.6670	.8952	1.1171	.7451	10
42° 00′	.6691	.9004	1.1106	.7431	48° 00′
10	.6713	.9057	1.1041	.7412	50
20	.6734	.9110	1.0977	.7392	40
30	.6756	.9163	1.0913	.7373	30
40	.6777	.9217	1.0850	.7353	20
50	.6799	.9271	1.0786	.7333	10
43° 00′	.6820	.9325	1.0724	.7314	47° 00′
10	.6841	.9380	1.0661	.7294	50
20	.6862	.9435	1.0599	.7274	40
30	.6884	.9490	1.0538	.7254	30
40	.6905	.9545	1.0477	.7234	20
50	.6926	.9601	1.0416	.7214	10
44° 00′	.6947	.9657	1.0355	.7193	46° 00′
10	.6967	.9713	1.0295	.7173	50
20	.6988	.9770	1.0235	.7153	40
30	.7009	.8827	1.0176	.7133	30
40	.7030	.9884	1.0117	.7112	20
50	.7050	.9942	1.0058	.7092	10
45° 00′	.7071	1.0000	1.0000	.7071	45° 00′
	Cosine	Cotan-gent	Tan-gent	Sine	Angle

Table XII. Logarithms*

N	0	1	2	3	4	5	6	7	8	9
10	0000	0043	0086	0128	0170	0212	0253	0294	0334	0374
11	0414	0453	0492	0531	0569	0607	0645	0682	0719	0755
12	0792	0828	0864	0899	0934	0969	1004	1038	1072	1106
13	1139	1173	1206	1239	1271	1303	1335	1367	1399	1430
14	1461	1492	1523	1553	1584	1614	1644	1673	1703	1732
15	1761	1790	1818	1847	1875	1903	1931	1959	1987	2014
16	2041	2068	2095	2122	2148	2175	2201	2227	2253	2279
17	2304	2330	2355	2380	2405	2430	2455	2480	2504	2529
18	2553	2577	2601	2625	2648	2672	2695	2718	2742	2765
19	2788	2810	2833	2856	2878	2900	2923	2945	2967	2989
20	3010	3032	3054	3075	3096	3118	3139	3160	3181	3201
21	3222	3243	3263	3284	3304	3324	3345	3365	3385	3404
22	3424	3444	3464	3483	3502	3522	3541	3560	3579	3598
23	3617	3636	3655	3674	3692	3711	3729	3747	3766	3784
24	3802	3820	3838	3856	3874	3892	3909	3927	3945	3962
25	3979	3997	4014	4031	4048	4065	4082	4099	4116	4133
26	4150	4166	4183	4200	4216	4232	4249	4265	4281	4298
27	4314	4330	4346	4362	4378	4393	4409	4425	4440	4456
28	4472	4487	4502	4518	4533	4548	4564	4579	4594	4609
29	4624	4639	4654	4669	4683	4698	4713	4728	4742	4757
30	4771	4786	4800	4814	4829	4843	4857	4871	4886	4900
31	4914	4928	4942	4955	4969	4983	4997	5011	5024	5038
32	5051	5065	5079	5092	5105	5119	5132	5145	5159	5172
33	5185	5198	5211	5224	5237	5250	5263	5276	5289	5302
34	5315	5328	5340	5353	5366	5378	5391	5403	5416	5428
35	5441	5453	5465	5478	5490	5502	5514	5527	5539	5551
36	5563	5575	5587	5599	5611	5623	5635	5647	5658	5670
37	5682	5694	5705	5717	5729	5740	5752	5763	5775	5786
38	5798	5809	5821	5832	5843	5855	5866	5877	5888	5899
39	5911	5922	5933	5944	5955	5966	5977	5988	5999	6010
40	6021	6031	6042	6053	6064	6075	6085	6096	6107	6117
N	0	1	2	3	4	5	6	7	8	9

* From W. W. Elliott and Edward R. C. Miles, *College Mathematics: A First Course*, 2nd Ed. New York: Prentice-Hall, Inc., 1951.

Table XII. Logarithms (Cont.)

N	0	1	2	3	4	5	6	7	8	9
40	6021	6031	6042	6053	6064	6075	6085	6096	6107	6117
41	6128	6138	6149	6160	6170	6180	6191	6201	6212	6222
42	6232	6243	6253	6263	6274	6284	6294	6304	6314	6325
43	6335	6345	6355	6365	6375	6385	6395	6405	6415	6425
44	6435	6444	6454	6464	6474	6484	6493	6503	6513	6522
45	6532	6542	6551	6561	6571	6580	6590	6599	6609	6618
46	6628	6637	6646	6656	6665	6675	6684	6693	6702	6712
47	6721	6730	6739	6749	6758	6767	6776	6785	6794	6803
48	6812	6821	6830	6839	6848	6857	6866	6875	6884	6893
49	6902	6911	6920	6928	6937	6946	6955	6964	6972	6981
50	6990	6998	7007	7016	7024	7033	7042	7050	7059	7067
51	7076	7084	7093	7101	7110	7118	7126	7135	7143	7152
52	7160	7168	7177	7185	7193	7202	7210	7218	7226	7235
53	7243	7251	7259	7267	7275	7284	7292	7300	7308	7316
54	7324	7332	7340	7348	7356	7364	7372	7380	7388	7396
55	7404	7412	7419	7427	7435	7443	7451	7459	7466	7474
56	7482	7490	7497	7505	7513	7520	7528	7536	7543	7551
57	7559	7566	7574	7582	7589	7597	7604	7612	7619	7627
58	7634	7642	7649	7657	7664	7672	7679	7686	7694	7701
59	7709	7716	7723	7731	7738	7745	7752	7760	7767	7774
60	7782	7789	7796	7803	7810	7818	7825	7832	7839	7846
61	7853	7860	7868	7875	7882	7889	7896	7903	7910	7917
62	7924	7931	7938	7945	7952	7959	7966	7973	7980	7987
63	7993	8000	8007	8014	8021	8028	8035	8041	8048	8055
64	8062	8069	8075	8082	8089	8096	8102	8109	8116	8122
65	8129	8136	8142	8149	8156	8162	8169	8176	8182	8189
66	8195	8202	8209	8215	8222	8228	8235	8241	8248	8254
67	8261	8267	8274	8280	8287	8293	8299	8306	8312	8319
68	8325	8331	8338	8344	8351	8357	8363	8370	8376	8382
69	8388	8395	8401	8407	8414	8420	8426	8432	8439	8445
70	8451	8457	8463	8470	8476	8482	8488	8494	8500	8506
N	0	1	2	3	4	5	6	7	8	9

Table XII. Logarithms (Cont.)

N	0	1	2	3	4	5	6	7	8	9
70	8451	8457	8463	8470	8476	8482	8488	8494	8500	8506
71	8513	8519	8525	8531	8537	8543	8549	8555	8561	8567
72	8573	8579	8585	8591	8597	8603	8609	8615	8621	8627
73	8633	8639	8645	8651	8657	8663	8669	8675	8681	8686
74	8692	8698	8704	8710	8716	8722	8727	8733	8739	8745
75	8751	8756	8762	8768	8774	8779	8785	8791	8797	8802
76	8808	8814	8820	8825	8831	8837	8842	8848	8854	8859
77	8865	8871	8876	8882	8887	8893	8899	8904	8910	8915
78	8921	8927	8932	8938	8943	8949	8954	8960	8965	8971
79	8976	8982	8987	8993	8998	9004	9009	9015	9020	9025
80	9031	9036	9042	9047	9053	9058	9063	9069	9074	9079
81	9085	9090	9096	9101	9106	9112	9117	9122	9128	9133
82	9138	9143	9149	9154	9159	9165	9170	9175	9180	9186
83	9191	9196	9201	9206	9212	9217	9222	9227	9232	9238
84	9243	9248	9253	9258	9263	9269	9274	9279	9284	9289
85	9294	9299	9304	9309	9315	9320	9325	9330	9335	9340
86	9345	9350	9355	9360	9365	9370	9375	9380	9385	9390
87	9395	9400	9405	9410	9415	9420	9425	9430	9435	9440
88	9445	9450	9455	9460	9465	9469	9474	9479	9484	9489
89	9494	9499	9504	9509	9513	9518	9523	9528	9533	9538
90	9542	9547	9552	9557	9562	9566	9571	9576	9581	9586
91	9590	9595	9600	9605	9609	9614	9619	9624	9628	9633
92	9638	9643	9647	9652	9657	9661	9666	9671	9675	9680
93	9685	9689	9694	9699	9703	9708	9713	9717	9722	9727
94	9731	9736	9741	9745	9750	9754	9759	9763	9768	9773
95	9777	9782	9786	9791	9795	9800	9805	9809	9814	9818
96	9823	9827	9832	9836	9841	9845	9850	9854	9859	9863
97	9868	9872	9877	9881	9886	9890	9894	9899	9903	9908
98	9912	9917	9921	9926	9930	9934	9939	9943	9948	9952
99	9956	9961	9965	9969	9974	9978	9983	9987	9991	9996
N	0	1	2	3	4	5	6	7	8	9

INDEX